D1445993

WILLY LEY

GAS GIANTS
THE LARGEST PLANETS

MCGRAW-HILL BOOK COMPANY
New York · Toronto · London · Sydney
St. Louis · San Francisco · Mexico · Panama

SOME OTHER BOOKS BY WILLY LEY

ROCKETS, MISSILES, AND
MEN IN SPACE
THE CONQUEST OF SPACE
THE EXPLORATION OF MARS
(WITH WERNHER VON BRAUN)
WATCHERS OF THE SKIES
ENGINEERS' DREAMS
DISCOVERY OF THE ELEMENTS
INSIDE THE ORBIT OF THE EARTH
VISITORS FROM AFAR: THE COMETS

Library of Congress Catalog Card Number: 76-98052

07-037637-9
07-037638-7

  34567890   VBVB   754

TABLE OF CONTENTS

ONE	A Family Of Planets	5
TWO	The Biggest Of Them All: Jupiter	19
THREE	A World With Rings	53
FOUR	"The First Comet Of 1781" (Uranus)	85
FIVE	Neptune And Its Former Moon	101
SIX	Beyond The Orbit Of Neptune	127
SEVEN	Appendix	135
EIGHT	Index	141

CHAPTER ONE

A FAMILY OF PLANETS

It would be wonderful if we were able to examine a solar system other than our own. Unfortunately there is no other sun close enough for us to see its planets. In a few cases we know that another star must have a "dark companion" because it does not move through space in a straight line. The gravitational pull of the unseen companion changes the straight line into a faintly wavy line.

But even in these cases—four of them are known—where the motion of a star betrays the presence of a dark companion, we cannot be sure that the companion is a large planet. It is possible that the companion is not really dark, but another sun whose light is too faint to register on the photographic plate. And even if the dark companion is a very large planet we do not know whether there are smaller planets in addition to the big one.

The reason why it would be so instructive to have a look at another solar system, preferably several systems, is that it would tell us whether our own system is typical or not. Do other solar systems show the division into two sub-systems of different types of planets that we have in ours? Or is our system an exception? The question is so important because it might change our thoughts about the origin of our solar system if we knew how other systems are organized.

The two sub-systems of our own solar system go under the simple names of "inner" and "outer" planets. Counting outward from the sun we have four planets which have it in common that they are fairly small but also have a high density. Our earth, the third from the sun, is the largest of these four inner planets.

Nearest to the sun is Mercury, orbiting the sun at a mean distance of 40 percent of the distance from the sun to the earth. It is a small planet with a diameter of 3100 miles, and it needs 88 (earth) days to complete one orbit. The next planet is Venus, with a diameter of 7600 miles. The distance of Venus from the sun is 72 percent of the earth's distance, and the time required to complete one orbit is 224.7 (earth) days. Then comes the earth, with a diameter of 7930 miles and an orbital period of 365¼ days. Finally there is Mars, 4200 miles in diameter, 1½ times as far from the sun as the earth and needing 687 (earth) days to complete one orbit. In Martian days, the orbital period is 668.6 days.

The mean distance of the earth from the sun is 93 million miles, the minimum distance is 1½ million miles less than that figure and the maximum distance is 1½ million miles more. But the figure of 93 million miles has another name, it is called the "astronomical unit," abbreviated as A.U. Astronomers use the astronomical unit as a measure of distance. They say that the distance of Mars is 1.5 A.U. while the distance of the largest planet in our system, Jupiter, is 5.2 A.U.

I know from lecture experience that many people wonder why the A.U. is in use at all. Why not just say so and so many million miles and be done with it? There are three reasons for using the A.U., the first of which is historical. Before 1780, when the length of the A.U. was not known, the guesses began at about 20 million miles and ranged up to about 50 million miles. But they were admittedly guesses, until Dr. Edmond Halley, who has the famous comet named after him suggested a method of measuring the length of the A.U. But this method involved seeing the planet Venus in front of the sun, and that is something that just does not happen very often. To be precise it happens twice per century, and these two Venus "transits," as they are called, happen eight years apart. The next Venus transit, after Halley's suggestion had been made, was not due until 1761, the one after that would be in 1769.

Until then nobody could know the true length of the A.U. But one of the three laws discovered by the German astronomer Johannes Kepler (who had died in 1630) was a formula by the use of which one could calculate the distance of a planet from the sun by its orbital period and comparing it with the orbital period of the earth and the distance of the earth from the sun.[1] Hence one could tell from the orbital period of Jupiter that it had to be 5.2 A.U. from the sun. The distance could not be expressed in miles, since nobody knew how many miles there were in one A.U., but at least you could say that Jupiter was five times as far from the sun than the earth.

[1] An example will be given in Chapter VI. For Kepler's three laws, see the Appendix.

The second reason for using the A.U. is that it keeps the figures smaller. Saturn is 886 million miles from the sun and Uranus 1782 million miles. Saying that Saturn is 9.54 A.U. and Uranus 19.18 A.U. from the sun is simpler and it also gives a better mental picture.

The third reason has to do with the planet's temperature, or rather with the amount of light and heat it receives from the sun. The amount of radiation received is inversely proportional to the square of the distance. In ordinary language this means that a body twice as far from the sun as another body receives only $1/2^2$ (or one quarter) as much radiation, a body three times as far receives only one ninth as much and so forth. Obviously these fractions can be expressed more simply by using the A.U. For example, Saturn, at 9.54 A.U. will receive $1/9.54^2$ or 1/91 as much light and heat as the earth.

Having clarified the meaning and the reasons for the use of the A.U. we can go back to the solar system. We have the four inner planets, at distances from 0.4 to 1.52 A.U.

Between 1.52 A.U. (the distance of Mars) and 5.2 A.U. (the distance of Jupiter) there is a wide gap which could easily accommodate a planet. For unknown reasons, it doesn't, that is, it does not accommodate *one* planet. Instead an enormous number of small bodies often called asteroids, but officially called Minor Planets, orbit the sun in that gap. The largest of them is named Ceres and it is only 485 miles in diameter. How many Minor Planets exist is not known. Close to 1400 of them have been identified and named; their total number is probably 20 times as large.

Next, at 5.2 A.U., we have Jupiter; at 9.54 A.U., Saturn; at 19.18 A.U., Uranus; and at 30.06 A.U., Neptune.[2] All four are enormous in volume but quite low in density (not much denser than water), and they appear to consist in the main of hydrogen and other gases, hence the collective name of Gas Giants.

This, then, is the overall arrangement of our solar system: four small, dense inner planets, a zone of planetary debris, as the dividing line, and four large, less dense outer planets.

Can this type of arrangement be typical of solar systems in general? I do not mean precise detail like *four* dense and *four* light planets. Also the belt of Minor Planets may be the result of a catastrophe that happened in our solar system but did not necessarily happen in other systems. I mean the general arrangement: small, dense

[2] Pluto is not mentioned here for two reasons. The first and obvious one is that it, being smaller than the earth, is not a gas giant. For the second reason see Chapter V.

planets near a sun and large, less dense planets in the outer reaches of the system. If our ideas about the origin of our solar system are correct, this general arrangement should hold true for other systems too.

The first man to think systematically about the origin of the solar system was the German philosopher Immanuel Kant (1724–1804), who wrote a small book about it in 1755. It had the title *General Natural History and Theory of the Heavens,* with a subtitle saying that it was written "in accordance with Newtonian principles." The subtitle shows that it was Sir Isaac Newton's main work that started Kant thinking. Sir Issac Newton (1642–1727), had published a book that is still called *Principia Mathematica* because it was originally written in Latin. In it Newton had proved that all the motions of all the bodies in space could be explained by two factors: gravity and inertia. "Gravity" meant that every body in space exerts an attraction on all other bodies; "inertia" meant that a body that is moving will continue its motion unless some force changes either the direction or the speed of its motion. The same is true, of course, if a body has zero motion, meaning that it is at rest. It will not start moving unless some force makes it do so.

This was enough to start Kant thinking. Kant had no trouble following Newton's mathematics, for mathematics had been his first study and for a number of years in his youth he could not make up his mind whether he would become a professor of mathematics or a professor of Latin. As everybody knows he became a great philosopher in the end. But his first published works dealt with theoretical astronomy.

Astronomers already knew that there were diffuse patches of light in the sky which could only be enormous clouds of gas and dust. Kant reasoned that such a cloud might be the origin of the solar system. Because of the mutual attraction of the particles, the cloud might contract and he assumed that the contraction would also cause it to rotate, if it did not rotate already. The condensation in the center would ultimately become the sun and the rapidly rotating sun would then throw matter into space which would become the planets.

Several decades later a French mathematician, Pierre Simon, Marquis de Laplace (1749–1827), evolved a similar idea and he worked it out mathematically in a manuscript which was to be just a long paper, but grew into a book of several volumes. After Laplace's death the two theories began to fuse and through most of the nineteenth century astronomers and other naturalists spoke about the Kant-Laplace theory. In its final form it looked like this: the gas and dust cloud might have had almost any shape before it started condensing. But as it condensed it also flattened out into a disk shape. Finally all the matter that had formed the original cloud was condensed into one body, the sun. The sun rotated rapidly and because of its fast rotation developed a bulge along its equator. Finally that bulge was thrown off into space to form a ring of matter. That ring condensed in turn, forming a planet. Quite often the ring broke into several pieces; the result was a planet and its moons.

When the first of these rings was thrown off the sun was still much larger than it is now. After throwing off the ring it condensed some more, its rotation speeded up, and another equatorial bulge developed. This process was repeated until all eight planets had been formed. By now the sun has reached a degree of condensation that cannot be increased very much anymore, hence the sun's rotation will not speed up again, and it cannot be expected that still another planet will be formed.

It was a fine theory while it lasted, but it did not last beyond the end of the nineteenth century. By then there were all kinds of questions, unanswerable at the time. One was how the sun manages to keep shining, losing energy all the time. That question could not be answered until atomic energy was discovered. Another question dealt with what physicists call "angular momentum" (which might also be called "quantity of rotation"). This concept is related to that of ordinary momentum, the energy of a moving body, say a bullet. Just as the moving bullet contains energy by virtue of its motion, a rotating wheel contains energy by virtue of the fact that it is rotating. Evidently a very large wheel has more "angular momentum" than a small wheel. The rotating sun has a certain amount of angular momentum: it compares to a wheel 865,000 miles in diameter that performs one rotation in 25 days. The planet earth needs one year per revolution, but it compares to a wheel 186 million miles in diameter. When physicists calculated the angular momentum for the sun on the one hand and for all the planets on the other, they discovered to their surprise that though the sun had about 98 percent of all the mass in the solar system, it had only 2 percent of all the angular momentum. The planets represented only 2 percent of the mass but they had 98 percent of the angular momentum.

This puzzle called the "distribution of the angular momentum," was insoluble in 1900 and some of its theoretical aspects are still under debate. But the first result of the recognition of this problem was that the Kant-Laplace theory had to be abandoned.

Even though the Kant-Laplace theory had been recognized as faulty the solar system still existed and its origin had to be explained in some manner. At least five major theories were formulated for this purpose during the first four decades of the present century. They all had to be discarded for one reason or another, and now we are back to the rotating dust and gas cloud.

But the new theory describes things somewhat differently. According to it, the main result of the condensation of the gas cloud is still the sun, but as the cloud condensed there was not just one condensation center in the middle. There were other smaller condensation centers in the rotating cloud, and the planets formed in these subsidiary condensation centers. They never were part of the sun (hence the question why the sun has so little angular momentum and the planets so much of it did not come up), and they were formed at the same time as the sun. They all kept shrinking by the mutual attraction of their particles, but at one point something happened in the sun that could not happen in the planets.

Yes, the term "in" the sun is correct, because this happening took place at the sun's center. When a gas is compressed, heat is generated in the process. Naturally the pressures, and with them the temperatures, are greater in a larger body. And when the temperature reaches a certain high value—say 20 million degrees—atomic fusion is started. The planets were too small to produce the pressures and temperatures that start the atomic fusion process. But in the sun it happened. Of course the sun had been shining, probably a dull red, before atomic fusion began, simply because it was a large and hot body. But when hydrogen atoms began fusing into helium atoms the sun began to be a "sun," shining brightly.

At that time the planets were probably still hot from their own condensation, and all of them were surrounded by enormous atmospheres—cloaks of gas not necessarily like our air. The atmosphere of the earth may have had a depth of several thousand miles. It is probable that even at that stage some planets looked and were larger than others (if you counted their atmospheres) but the differences in size were less pronounced than they are now. Then the heat coming from the sun caused a change. The planets near the sun were heated enough so that their original large atmospheres were dissipated in space by the sun's action (see Chapter 3, pages 69–70).

But the outer planets were far enough from the sun so that their atmospheres did not undergo much heating and were retained. In other words the outer planets, probably larger to begin with, kept their original atmospheres. The inner planets lost them so that only their rocky cores were left. The atmosphere we now have here on earth is a "secondary" atmosphere, one that formed after the original atmosphere was lost.

If this theory is correct it explains why the outer planets are large and the inner planets are small.

And this is the reason for the opening sentence of this chapter. If we could examine another solar system and if we found that that other system also has large outer planets and small inner planets, we would know whether this theory is correct or not.

Since we do not yet have the means of examining another solar system we can only assume that this theory is correct; at least we do not know of any facts that contradict it.

The gas giants, then, are planets that still are as they were when the sun started blazing.

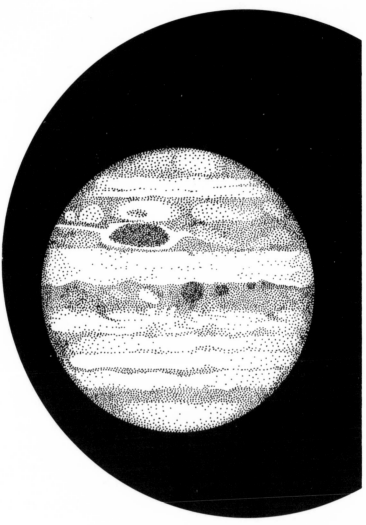

Fig. 1   Telescopic view of Jupiter

CHAPTER TWO

THE BIGGEST OF THEM ALL: JUPITER

The planets were assigned by the Romans to various gods and goddesses. The planet Jupiter, when Venus is not in the sky, is the brightest planet. The Romans identified it with Jupiter, their highest god.

When the early Romans had to swear a solemn oath, they did so under the open sky at night and swore by "father Jove," in Latin *Iovis pater*. Scholars suppose that a contraction of these two words resulted in the current name of the planet.

Jupiter, the innermost of the four gas giants, is also the largest. Its volume is 1317 times the volume occupied by the earth. Jupiter weighs as much as 318 earths; in fact its mass is larger than that of all the other planets put together. The total mass of all the planets is about 128 earth masses; since Jupiter is equal to 318 earth masses it follows that Jupiter has nearly 2½ times as much matter concentrated in its bulk as all the others *and* their moons.

In most respects Jupiter is typical of the gas giants, but because of its mass and its relative nearness to the sun it also shows a number of features that are different from those of the others. Jupiter is the only gas giant—in fact the only planet other than the earth—that is known to have a magnetic field. Of the four inner planets we know that Venus and Mars do not have a magnetic field and it is considered unlikely that Mercury does. We simply don't know whether the three other gas giants do or not. Jupiter is the only planet—again the only one other than the earth—that sends out sporadic bursts of natural radio noise. And Jupiter is the only gas giant that *may* have fairly high temperatures in some layers of its atmosphere. The three others are definitely cold all the way through.

Now for the "family resemblances." All four are large. Jupiter is the most massive, Saturn has about one-third the mass of Jupiter, while Uranus and Neptune are about equal in size and mass, each with a mass about one-sixth that of Saturn. All of them consist of a comparatively small rocky core, of unknown size, surrounded by a "mantle" of either ice or solid gas with a thickness of thousands of miles, surrounded in turn by an atmosphere thousands of miles in depth. The atmospheres consist mainly of hydrogen gas, with small amounts of helium and still smaller amounts of ammonia and methane.

Older books usually give figures for the surface temperatures: minus 100° Fahrenheit for Jupiter, minus 250° Fahrenheit for Saturn, and minus 400° Fahrenheit for Uranus and Neptune. These are pretty figures but all they really say is that the temperatures are very low. And whether they apply to the surfaces can be questioned on the simple grounds that we do not know how deep the atmospheres of the gas giants really are, which means, of course, that we do not know where the surface begins.

The gas giants all have a fairly high albedo, ranging from about 42 to about 52. *Albedo* is a Spanish word that somehow got into the astronomical vocabulary; taken literally it means "whiteness." It is used to refer to the amount of sunlight that is reflected by the planet's surface or cloud layer. Looking at a body in space can be quite deceptive when it comes to albedo. Our silvery moon has an albedo of only 7, for its surface swallows up 93 percent of the sunlight received. To establish the figure for the albedo we have to find out first how much sunlight is received by the body and then one has to measure how much of it is reflected.

All four gas giants have rather regular orbits. Their orbits are ellipses, but they are ellipses that deviate so little from a circle that if we tried to show the differences in a drawing of a size that could be reproduced in a book, they would disappear in the thickness of the line. The orbits of the gas giants are regular in another sense too: they show very little inclination to the plane of the orbit of the earth, called the ecliptic. The low inclination means that, to the eye of an observer on earth, they stay nicely in the zodiac, the twelve constellations that are in the plane of the ecliptic.

Everybody who has ever looked for Jupiter or Saturn in the sky knows that the two planets sometimes look considerably brighter than at other times. This is due to the relative positions of the planets in their orbits. Jupiter will look brightest when it is "in opposition." This is really an astrological term that has been kept in use by astronomers because it is a clear and simple concept: a planet is "in opposition" when it occupies a position in the sky that is directly opposite from the position occupied by the sun. The opposite of opposition occurs when the planet occupies the same spot in the sky as the sun; the planet is behind the sun and cannot be observed from the earth for that reason.

The line-up in space looks like this:
"in opposition":
Jupiter—the earth—the sun
"in conjunction":
Jupiter—the sun—the earth

The next opposition of Jupiter will take place on April 21, 1970; the next conjunction after that opposition, on November 9, 1970.

It is very easy to gain an idea of the distance from the earth to one of the gas giants if you know the distance of the planet in question from the sun, so for the sake of small figures we'll express the distances in A.U. Jupiter is 5.2 A.U. from the sun. If it is in opposition, the planet and the earth are both on the same side of the sun, hence the distance from earth to Jupiter is 5.2 minus 1 A.U. When Jupiter is in conjunction it is on the other side of the sun, hence the distance is 5.2 plus 1 A.U. This reasoning goes for all the others, too.

Let us say now that we have just observed an

opposition of Jupiter. How long do we have to wait until the next opposition takes place? Well, Jupiter needs 11.9 years to complete one of its orbits, or, expressed in another way, it needs 11.9 earth years to traverse a full circle of 360 degrees of arc. Hence, during one earth year it traverses an arc of 30.25 degrees or about $\frac{1}{12}$ of 360 degrees. The earth, during that period, has traversed a full circle. But the three bodies, Jupiter, the earth, and the sun, do not yet form a straight line again, for Jupiter will be 30.25 degrees of arc "ahead" when the earth returns to its original position.

Now the earth has to catch up and the earth moves not quite one degree of arc per day in its orbit. Hence the next opposition takes place about $365\frac{1}{4} + 31 = 396\frac{1}{4}$ days after the first opposition. In reality the time is a bit longer because we made our quick calculation with rounded-off figures. The mean interval of oppositions of Jupiter is 398.88 or just about 399 days. This period, the interval between oppositions, is called the "synodic period" of the planet.

Look at the synodic periods of the other gas giants too because we'll find out something very interesting in doing so.

Saturn needs $29\frac{1}{2}$ years to complete one orbit, partly because its orbit is longer, partly because it moves more slowly in its orbit. The farther a planet is from the sun the slower its orbital motion. (This also holds true for the moons of a planet—the farther away, the slower.) Now since Saturn needs 29½ years to traverse a full circle of 360 degrees of arc it follows that it will traverse only 12.6 degrees of arc in one earth year. "Catch-up" time for the earth will be about 13 days, so the synodic period of Saturn is 378.1 days.

Now let's check on Uranus, which needs 84 years to complete one orbit. In one earth year it moves only 4.3 degrees of arc, so that the catch-up time is around 4½ days; the next opposition will take place 1 year plus 4½ days after the previous opposition. Neptune needs 164 years to complete one orbit; in one earth year it moves about 2.2 degrees of arc so that the catch-up time is about 2½ days. It can easily be seen that the time interval between oppositions grows smaller the farther the planet is from the sun. For a planet so far away that it shows no perceptible motion the synodic period would be precisely one earth year.

Everything that has been said about oppositions applies to conjunctions too, of course. Jupiter becomes unobservable for some time at 400-day intervals, Saturn at 380-day intervals, and

Uranus and Neptune become unobservable at yearly intervals.

If our eyes were good enough to see Jupiter about half as large as the full moon, its name would be *rhabdotos* if it had been named by the Greeks, or *virgatus* if named by the Romans, both words meaning "striped." The first thing an observer notices when he sees Jupiter through a good telescope (four inches and above) is the large number of dark stripes around the planet, running parallel to each other like degrees of latitude on a globe.

While the fine detail of each of these stripes changes constantly the stripes themselves are fairly permanent, though it happens that two of them merge. Specialists distinguish no less than sixteen "belts" and "zones," as shown in Fig. 2. The brighter lines are called zones and the dark ones are called belts which is a bit confusing because "zone" is really a Greek word meaning "belt." But Jupiter is a confusing planet, as we'll soon find out.

Prominent markings that can last for a number of days often appear in the belts. It was an obvious thought to use these markings to determine the period of rotation. As soon as telescopes grew powerful enough for the purpose it became clear that Jupiter rotated in a little less than 10 hours. But when it came to establish what this "little less" was in figures the difficulties began. It was not even a case of one expert finding one figure and another expert another; the same experts found different figures.

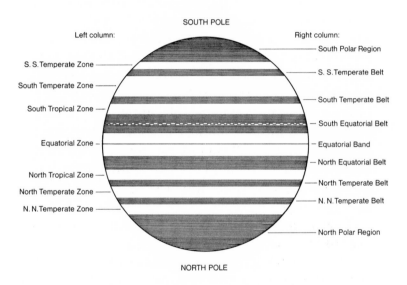

Fig. 2   The zones and belts of Jupiter

Giovanni Domenico Cassini, observing Jupiter from Paris around the middle of the seventeenth century, found the value to be 9 hours 56 minutes. But a short time later, using another prominent marking, he found it to be 9 hours 50 minutes. About fifteen years later, in 1779, William Herschel, observing from Bath in England, tried to find a more precise value; it turned out to be 9 hours, 50 minutes, 48 seconds. One year later he repeated his determination and his first observation informed him that he had been a full 5 minutes off. It was 9 hours, 55 minutes, and a few seconds. Quite naturally he reasoned that he had made a mistake one year before, or else that he had made a mistake just now. So he looked for other spots and repeated his observations and calculations quite a number of times. Each time he found that the period of rotation was about 4 minutes shorter than an even 10 hours; the mean of all his observations was 9 hours, 55 minutes and 40 seconds.

Now which, a modern reader is apt to ask, is the correct value?

The somewhat disconcerting answer is that both values are correct. It depends on where you look for a moving spot in Jupiter's cloud bands. If you pick a spot near the planet's equator it always works out to 9 hours, 50 minutes, 30 seconds. But if you go by spots more than 10 degrees of latitude (north or south) from the equator the figure becomes 9 hours, 55 minutes, and a fraction over 40 seconds. The higher figure is called "System II," while the equatorial figure is called "System I."

Since we do not see the planet's surface but only the top of a cloud layer, it is easy to understand that the "spots," which are in reality enormous cloud masses, will move with somewhat different velocities. But why the atmospheric current over the equator should persistently race ahead by five minutes per rotation is not at all easy to understand. By using the term "race ahead" I have already indicated that the general opinion among planetary observers was that "System II" represented the rotation of the body of the planet.

But it seemed impossible to prove it, until the English astronomer E. J. Reese had a new thought. All the previous observers had based their calculations on the motion of the spots, which, of course, might involve drifting in a cloud layer. Reese thought that he could get a more accurate picture by neglecting the motion of spots but checking carefully on their first appearance. He assumed that the appearance of a new spot was the result of some event farther down. If we were talking about the earth we might say a volcanic eruption. However, since we have no way of knowing (and some reasons for doubting) that there are volcanoes on Jupiter, we have to use the term "explosion" and leave it to the future to substitute a more correct word.

Reese began checking records of the sudden appearance of new spots. He found six of them, fortunately all in the same latitude, the South Equatorial Belts. There had been one each in 1919, 1928, 1949, and 1952. In 1943 there had been two, both during the month of February. Reese called them 1943 A and 1943 B. If each of these spots had been caused by an "explosion" in the same place on the surface of the planet, as Reese supposed, then the times of the appearances of these spots (disregarding later drift) should furnish a clue to the rotational period of the body of the planet. Reese first calculated a period of 9 hours, 54 minutes and $52\frac{1}{2}$ seconds. This fitted all of the appearances except the spot 1943 B. Reese began to suspect that these six explosions, though they all seemed from a distance to have taken place under the same latitude, might not in fact have done so. In other words the source of all six spots might not have been the same.

An assumed period of rotation of 9 hours, 55 minutes, 42.66 seconds also fitted well, but then two spots were out of step, namely 1919 and 1943 B. And the discrepancy was not just a question of a few minutes which might be put down as an inaccuracy in observation. It was a difference of nearly 2½ hours. But then Reese noticed that both spots differed by the same number of minutes in the same direction. Assuming one cause was responsible for four of the spots, and another for the two others, all the observations could be made to fit a period of 9 hours, 55 minutes, 42.66 seconds; if that period was correct, then the cause for the two spots was located in the same latitude, as the cause of the four other spots, but 88 degrees of longitude away from it.

This work proved that the planet did rotate in accordance with "System II," the areas of Jupiter's atmosphere which lie at a distance from the equator.

Because of its fast rotation Jupiter's atmosphere is flattened at the poles. Therefore, two figures must be given to express its diameters, one for the diameter from pole to pole and the other for the diameter from one point on the equator to the opposite point on the equator. (See the table in the Appendix for these figures; the diameter of the planet's body is unknown.)

The color of Jupiter is difficult to describe. To the naked eye it is white, in the telescope the belts look gray, but sometimes they appear brown, and occasionally brown with a pronounced red hue. A given belt will not look the same color after a number of years; there is, in

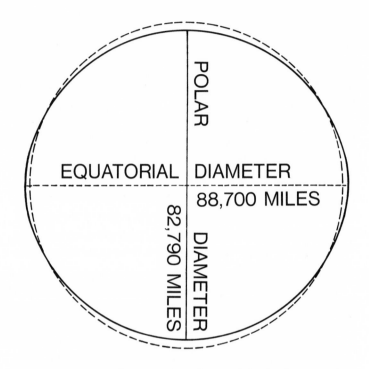

POLAR

EQUATORIAL DIAMETER
88,700 MILES

82,790 MILES

DIAMETER

Fig. 3   How Jupiter has been flattened by its fast rotation.
The broken circle shows what shape (namely that
of a perfect sphere) it would have if it did not rotate.

fact, evidence that the belts change color period-
ically; the periodicity of the color change is
about the same as the orbital period of the
planet. No doubt there is an explanation for
these periodic color changes, but we don't know
this explanation yet, to our regret.

When, eighty years ago, astronomers tried to fit their observations into a comprehensive picture of the planet, they arrived at a simple conclusion. There was the violent activity in its atmosphere all the time, there was the reddish hue (sometimes more pronounced than at other times), there was the low density of the planet as a whole. The logical conclusion was that Jupiter had not yet lived through its period of excessive heat. It evidently was a planet still in the process of condensation. If it had a solid crust on top of its molten interior that crust must still be very thin, breaking up in places now and then and causing the clouds to glow red.

"Jupiter has only recently ceased to be a small secondary sun in our solar system" according to many books and articles of that period. And in August 1878 this view was bolstered by what seemed to be a totally new event. In that month the phenomenon known as the Red Spot was observed. Twenty degrees of latitude to the south of the equator a large elliptical spot appeared, which could quickly be determined to measure 30,000 miles in length, with its greatest width between 7,000 and 8,000 miles. This new spot differed from all the others not only in being much larger, but also in being bright brick red in color.

The explanation seemed simple. A few days before the Red Spot was seen a very large meteorite must have struck Jupiter, breaking a hole through the thin crust and causing liquid magma from the interior to flood an enormous area. The lava-flooded area on the surface might not be as regular as the Red Spot in outline, because the Red Spot was just the glow of the molten magma reflected in Jupiter's clouds.

Then two things happened that showed this explanation to be wrong. First, the Red Spot did not stay put in the same place. For a while one could salvage the original explanation by assuming that the molten lava had melted more of the solid crust in one direction, while it had solidified and grown dark at the other end. But after the Red Spot had drifted for more than its own length this explanation became absurd.

Next, it was discovered that the Red Spot was not new. It had been seen before, sometimes as a red spot, sometimes as a gray spot of the same dimensions and in the same latitude. Two drawings made by Cassini in 1672 and 1691 showed a large round spot in the proper latitude. But Cassini had not said that the spot was red; presumably it wasn't in his time. Robert Hooke, in 1664, stated that he had seen a dark spot in the southern hemisphere of Jupiter, but he did not draw it or at least did not publish a drawing. The German as-

seen it on two different occasions before the First World War when it was the color of lilac blossoms. Some of these color changes may not have been real but may have been caused by a very high haze in our own atmosphere. For instance, soon after the "discovery" of the Red Spot the volcano Rakata on the island of Krakatoa in the Sunda Strait blew up and filled the upper atmosphere with fine volcanic dust that did not settle for years. The dust could have caused the Red Spot to look violet.

The drifting of the Red Spot makes it clear that it is something floating in Jupiter's atmosphere, a concept that has been nicknamed the "raft theory." Some theorists assume that the "raft" is egg-shaped and as thick as it is wide, while others visualize a flat body which must be curved to correspond with the curvature of the planet. While we do not know what substances compose this raft, the concept has the advantage that it can explain the Red Spot's color changes. Assuming that its normal color is red, it would seem to fade and lose color when it is submerged under twenty or thirty miles of nearly opaque Jovian atmosphere.

And that brings us to the composition of the planet itself.

The old idea that Jupiter might still be in the

molten stage did not stand up well even under the simplest mathematical analysis. Molten rock is a fairly dense substance, much denser than Jupiter's overall density of 1.33 times that of water. To account for such a low density it was necessary to assume that there were a thousand miles or more of atmosphere below the cloud layer and nobody was quite willing to do that.

It was in 1923 that the high temperature of Jupiter was disproved and the concept of the gas giants was first evolved. The disproof of the high temperature came from two quarters. Dr. Donald H. Menzel of Harvard University did the mathematical work, basing it on temperature measurements made by two other American astronomers (F. W. W. Coblentz and C. O. Lampland), and found that the temperature of the clouds had to be somewhere near *minus* 165° Fahrenheit.

At the same time Dr. Harold Jeffreys in England speculated that if Jupiter had the same age as the earth it would have radiated all its heat away by now and would be solid. Of course naturally radioactive substances produce heat, but if Jupiter was still liquid because of radioactive elements it would have to contain 10,000 times as much uranium and thorium as the earth, an unlikely assumption. The natural conclusion from

Jeffreys' first assumption was a rocky planet 25,000 miles in diameter with an atmosphere 32,000 miles deep. That did not seem likely either, so Jeffreys wondered whether the bulk of the planet might not be ice. To produce the observed mass and overall density of Jupiter the rocky core would have to have a diameter of about 28,500 miles, the ice mantle would have to be 11,000 miles thick and the atmosphere would have to have a depth of 3700 miles.[2]

Ten years after Wildt, Dr. W. H. Ramsey startled everybody by pointing out that Jupiter might consist of hydrogen only. In a body as large as Jupiter the pressures must be enormous and just hydrogen does something surprising under high pressures. Normally the lightest gas, it acquires a density of about one third that of water if the pressure rises to 800,000 atmospheres. A little beyond that point hydrogen changes its structure and acquires what has been called its "metallic phase," with a density $9/10$ of that of water.

Well, pure hydrogen did not quite produce

[2] In 1938 Dr. Rupert Wildt made fresh calculations. According to Wildt, the rocky core would be nearly 19,000 miles in diameter and the ice mantle 17,000 miles thick. An outer shell of compressed gases not quite 8000 miles thick would rest on the ice mantle, and the truly gaseous atmosphere would be only 20 or 30 miles deep.

figures agreeing with reality, so Ramsey calculated the density of mixtures of hydrogen and helium in various ratios. A mixture of 1 atom of helium for every 22 atoms of hydrogen comes out about right, but everybody feels that there must

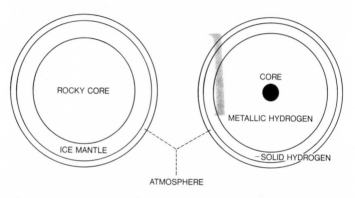

ROCKY CORE

ICE MANTLE

CORE

METALLIC HYDROGEN

SOLID HYDROGEN

ATMOSPHERE

Fig. 5   Two cross sections through Jupiter. The one on the
left is based on the calculations of Dr. Harold Jef-
fries in 1924 with a rocky core 57,160 miles in diameter. In the 1967 concept the rocky core has shrunk
to about the size of the earth and the ice has been
replaced by solid gases.

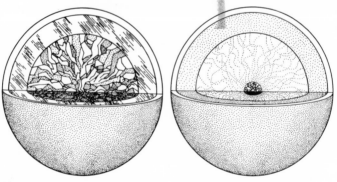

be a rocky core, though this core may not be much bigger than the earth.

So the modern picture of the make-up of Jupiter portrays it as a rocky core, maybe 10,000 miles in diameter, then a deep mantle of "metallic hydrogen," then a layer of solid compressed hydrogen, and then an atmosphere consisting mainly of hydrogen and helium that may be about 50 miles deep. The clouds are "impurities" in the hydrogen atmosphere, mostly methane and ammonia, probably existing as clouds of frozen crystals.

The same picture applies to the other three gas giants.

In the case of Jupiter the make-up of the atmosphere could not be proved for a long time, because both hydrogen and helium are indetectable when cold. But in 1952 the planet Jupiter would cover up a star and astronomers waited eagerly, since they would then be able to see how the star was gradually dimmed as it was seen through the upper layers of Jupiter's atmosphere. The decrease in brightness could be used to calculate the average weight of the molecules making up that atmosphere. The work was not easy, but the final result was that the "average molecular weight" came out as 3.3 units; just the right weight for a mixture of hydrogen and helium. (Our atmosphere consisting mainly of nitrogen and oxygen has a molecular weight of 29.)

In 1955 Jupiter produced another surprise: it was found to emit radio noise. The discovery was made by American scientists of the Carnegie Institute (Drs. B. F. Burke and F. L. Franklin), but it was an Australian scientist, Dr. C. A. Shain, who thoroughly investigated the phenomenon. He not only listened for such noises, he also had the records searched for unidentified radio noise in the past, attributed to unknown terrestrial sources. He found two series long enough to check for rotation, and discovered that they had rotated with System II. The two series had originated in the South Temperate Belt, which had shown several white spots at the time.

A postscript to this discovery was written in April, 1969, because of artificial satellite Explorer-XXXVIII. This satellite has two long pairs of antennas, which, put together, are longer than the Empire State Building is tall. Explorer-XXXVIII discovered that the earth sends out bursts of radio noise that are surprisingly similar to those emitted by Jupiter. They have very low frequencies (and therefore long wavelengths), are intense, and occur in rapid but sporadic bursts.

A tentative explanation of the origin of the

radio waves from Jupiter is that sub-atomic particles such as protons and electrons enter the Jovian atmosphere with a very high velocity, not much slower than the velocity of light. What is not generally known is that the figure always quoted for the velocity of light (186,000 miles per second) refers to the velocity of light in a vacuum. In certain gas mixtures it is less so that the sub-atomic particles actually travel faster than light in that atmosphere. That this can happen was found for the first time in 1934 by the Russian scientist Pavel Alexeyevitch Cerenkov[3] who received a Nobel Prize for his discovery. The particle then produces a wake of eerie blue light, naturally called Cerenkov radiation. Very likely it also produces radio waves.

Since the velocity of light has just been mentioned it is only fair to explain next that the concept of the velocity of light is largely due to Jupiter, specifically its four large moons. These moons are called the Galilean satellites because Galileo Galilei discovered them in 1610. They are easy to observe and Cassini, as a young man, had kept a careful record of their eclipses. Later Cassini moved to Paris and later still Christiaan Huygens arrived there accompanied by a young

[3] Pronounced tshay-REN-kov.

Danish astronomer named Ole Römer. Römer read Cassini's notes and saw that the intervals between these eclipses grew longer as the two planets earth and Jupiter drew apart and that they grew shorter when the distance between them became shorter.

Römer reasoned that the light from these satellites (reflected sunlight) had to travel greater or shorter distances to reach earth because of the shifting distances between the planets. If light needed time to travel, not only could the changing intervals between the eclipses of Jupiter's moons be explained, it would also be possible to calculate how fast light traveled. He worked this out, finding a figure reasonably close to the correct one.

He told Cassini about it.

Cassini refused to believe it; it was one of the few cases where he was wrong.

In the meantime there had been a major wrangle about the proper name for the four Galilean satellites. Galilei had wanted to name them the "stars of the Medici" but nobody wanted to go along with this.

On the other hand, Herr Simon Mayr in Germany who called himself Simon Marius, claimed to have seen the four satellites a month or so before Galilei. It is possible that he did, but he

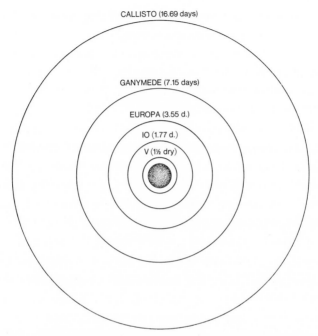

Fig. 6 The five inner moons of Jupiter; orbits are drawn to scale.

must not have realized what they were or else he would, at the very least, have written a letter to his friend Johannes Kepler. In any event, Marius suggested that the four satellites should be named after the four loves of Jupiter: Io, Europa, Ganymede, and Callisto. Galilei would hear none of this, especially since he considered Marius an impostor. Instead he decided to just number them. Kepler had sided with Marius.

Cassini sided with Galilei, and for a century or so only the numbers were used.

Then the four mythological names suggested by Marius slowly came into use. The whole thing was revived in September 1892. Edward Emerson Barnard discovered a fifth satellite of Jupiter which orbited inside the orbit of the nearest of the Galilean satellites. Barnard received lots of suggestions for a name but refused them all. People who wrote him suggested that "the fifth satellite" be named this or that. So, Barnard reasoned, why not call it "the fifth satellite?"

Camille Flammarion in France, founder of the French Astronomical Society, suggested the name Amalthea, the nursemaid of Jupiter. Barnard rejected the suggestion, but by now most astronomers used the name though some made footnotes saying that the name is "not official." [4]

In the course of the discussions on whether the fifth satellite should be given a name or should just be left numbered, one of the proponents of the numbering system made the remark that numbers had a great advantage. If still another satellite of Jupiter should be discovered there would be no doubt about its name. It would be named "J-VI."

J-VI was discovered in December, 1904, by

[4] An "official name" is given by the discoverer, or approved by the discoverer.

Charles Dillon Perrine, working at Lick Observatory. Only two months later the same observer found J-VII. J-VIII was added in 1908 by P. J. Melotte of the Royal Observatory. When the astronomical computers—which, at that time, were still human—went to work on its orbit they found that J-VIII moved in a direction opposite to those of the other moons. This indicated that Jupiter had more than one family of satellites. The farthest of the Galilean satellites, Callisto, moved at a distance of a little over one million miles away from Jupiter, while the two satellites discovered by Perrine orbited the planet at a distance of more than seven million miles. Melotte's J-VIII was more than twice as far from Jupiter as J-VI.

In 1914 Seth B. Nicholson of Mt. Wilson Observatory discovered J-IX, which was as far from Jupiter as Melotte's J-VIII and also moved the "wrong way." Nicholson then discovered J-X in 1938; it turned out to belong to "Perrine's group." Nicholson made two further discoveries, J-XI in 1938 and J-XII in 1951, both of them belonging to the outermost group. Nicholson, incidentally, felt that his steady photographic surveys of the Jovian system would have disclosed any still undiscovered satellites if they were large enough to register on a photographic plate.

There are clearly three groups, the inner group of five satellites fairly close to the planet, the group of three at about seven million miles, and another group of four at about fourteen million miles.

Only the four Galilean satellites are large enough so that surface markings can be seen. These markings confirm a suspicion held by Cassini, namely that all the moons of all the planets behave like our own moon: they always face the same hemisphere toward their planet. This is because their orbital periods and their periods of rotation on their axes are the same.

As for the two outer groups of small satellites it is generally believed that they were once independent members of the asteroid belt which were "captured" by Jupiter so that they now orbit the planet, instead of the sun directly.

That Jupiter greatly disturbs the tiny worlds in the asteroid belt is clear from another set of facts, too. In 1906, just after Perrine's two discoveries, Professor Max Wolf of the observatory of the University of Heidelberg, announced the discovery of one more asteroid, numero 588, later named Achilles. When its orbit was calculated from the positions given by Wolf it turned out to be nearly circular, which in itself is fairly unusual for an asteroid. But then it was found that,

SATELLITES OF JUPITER, 1970
CONFIGURATIONS OF SATELLITES 1-1V
FOR DECEMBER
UNIVERSAL TIME

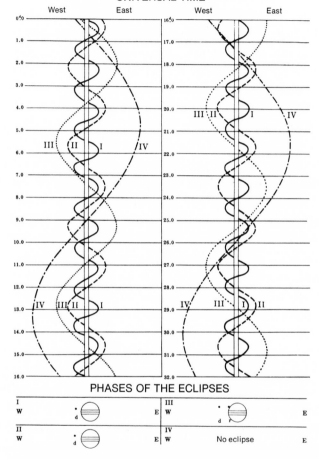

PHASES OF THE ECLIPSES

Representation of the orbits of the four large moons of Jupiter, showing the positions in which they can be seen through a telescope during the month of December, 1970.

Fig. 7

(From the *Nautical Almanac* for 1970)

49

since it moved at the same distance from the sun as Jupiter, it plainly moved in Jupiter's own orbit. While the computers were still wondering whether Wolf had given them a wrong position —highly unlikely for a man of his experience— the news came from Sweden that the newly discovered asteroid, Jupiter, and the sun formed an almost perfect equilateral triangle.

Now a little more than 230 years earlier a French scientist, Joseph Louis Lagrange, had written a book on methods of calculating the mutual attractions of more than two bodies in space. In the course of his mathematical research he had found that three bodies could form a stable configuration if two conditions held true. One was that one of the three bodies should be quite small, compared to the other two; the second condition was that they form an equilateral triangle. Achilles, Jupiter and the sun obviously did.

Of course there could be two equilateral triangles (Fig. 8), one in which the small body moved ahead of Jupiter and one in which the small body trailed Jupiter in its orbit. Achilles preceded Jupiter, was there another asteroid that trailed it? Max Wolf provided the answer during the same year. Asteroid numero 617 did. Max Wolf named it Patroclus, Achilles' comrade in the Trojan War.

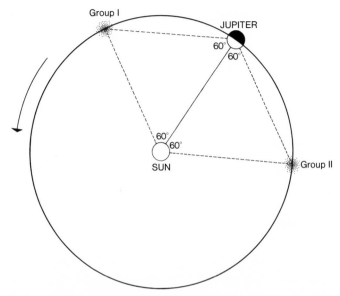

Fig. 8   The locations of the "Trojan asteroids" in Jupiter's orbit. The whole system forms two equilateral triangles. The asteroids oscillate around the points of the triangles; they might be 5 degrees of arc ahead of, or behind, these points.
Asteroids in Group I: Achilles, Hector, Nestor, Agamemnon, Odysseus, Heid 60 and Heid 61
Asteroids in Group II: Patroclus, Priamus, Aeneas, Anchises, Troilus, Ajax and Diomedes

Since then a total of nine asteroids near Achilles and a total of eight near Patroclus have been discovered; they are collectively known as the "Trojan asteroids," since all of them have been given names from Homer's *Iliad* that recounts the siege and fall of Troy.

Jupiter, as has been said earlier, is a confusing planet.

It may violate the rule that the surfaces of the gas giants must be cold. As Professor Carl Sagan of Harvard pointed out in 1961, the atmosphere of Jupiter should be opaque to infrared (heat) rays from the sun, but transparent to visible light. Now if the *surface* of Jupiter is opaque to visible light (something we don't know because we do not know its nature) it will be heated, because an opaque substance will absorb the energy of radiation directed on it. In turn it will emit infrared rays. But since the atmosphere of Jupiter is opaque to infrared, that heat cannot escape from the planet but stays trapped. In time enough heat may accumulate, and, to quote Sagan, "the possibility arises that water or ammonia seas exist on Jupiter."

It may be useful to stress that this reasoning applies to Jupiter only; the other gas giants are too far from the sun to receive enough light for this effect to take place. Whether Jupiter's surface actually is covered by a liquid of some kind cannot be decided by observation and photography. A space probe that can enter the Jovian atmosphere and land on the planet will be needed to settle this problem.

There are still discoveries to be made!

CHAPTER THREE

A WORLD WITH RINGS

Astronomical observatories, like all other public institutions, must see to it that their public relations are maintained. One way of doing this is to schedule a number of "visitor's nights" per year. The astronomer in charge can do something for the public by scheduling visitor's night carefully. It should be a night when the moon is approximately a half moon (unimportant whether it is waxing or waning), because then the mountains make beautiful shadows and the moon looks more impressive through the telescope than when it is nearly full. Hopefully one of the major planets will be in the sky; Jupiter's four large moons always look impressive to somebody who has never seen them before.

Best of all is Saturn high in the sky, for Saturn, seen through a good telescope, is one of the most beautiful sights one can behold. The reason is, of course, the rings that surround the planet. Even if one has seen them often they remain something that does not seem to be quite credible.

They were even more incredible to the early observers whose telescopes were not yet good enough to show the rings clearly. Galileo Galilei

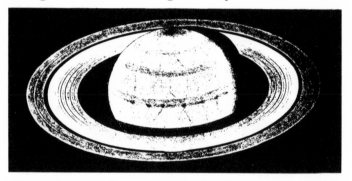

Fig. 9   Saturn as it was drawn by Percival Lowell in March, 1915. At that time the rings were as "open" as they can be, seen from the earth.

first thought that Saturn was accompanied by two large moons. The rings must have been wide open as seen from earth at the time, and their expanse on either side of the planet looked like two round bodies to Galilei. It must be kept in mind that Galilei did not expect to see a ring around the planet because no other planet has one.

At a later date, when Galilei tried to check up on the two "moons," he could not see them at all. The rings of Saturn must have been in the "edge-on" position, and in that position they disappear even in far more powerful telescopes than were in existence then. All Galilei could do was to wonder what had happened to the two moons. If there had been only one he could have concluded that it was behind Saturn along the line of sight from earth. But it was not likely that *both* moons would be behind the planet and Galilei made a worried note, wondering whether Saturn, like its namesake, "might have swallowed its children." He never solved the puzzle; the truth was discovered fourteen years after his death.

However, we have to begin with the planet itself.

Saturn was the seventh planet known in classical antiquity, but it was the seventh planet only because the ancients also counted the moon and the sun as planets. Their list, counting outward from the earth which was assumed to be in the center, read: the moon, Mercury, Venus, the sun, Mars, Jupiter and Saturn. The ancients knew that Saturn was the planet farthest from the earth because it moved more slowly among the fixed stars than any other planet. They considered Saturn the god of agriculture; the name of the planet is derived from *satus* which means grain that has been set aside for sowing. Of course they could have had no idea about its size; they only knew that it was easily visible and could be recognized by its slightly yellowish color.

We now know that Saturn is the second largest and the second most massive planet in our solar system. It has been mentioned in the preceding chapter that Jupiter has more mass than all the other planets combined. If you disregard Jupiter the same holds true for Saturn. Without Jupiter it is Saturn that has more mass than all the other planets combined. It weighs 95 times as much as the earth and its volume is such that it would need 793 earths to take up the same space. Since its volume is so great, the overall density of the planet is low; the planet weighs only seven tenths as much as the same volume of water. It is the only planet in the solar system which, taken as a whole, is lighter than water.

This indicates that its rocky core must be even smaller than the rocky core of Jupiter. But, as we have seen in the discussion of Jupiter's core there are so many uncertainties that it is impossible to arrive at accurate figures.

Because Saturn rotates on its axis almost as fast as Jupiter the body of the planet is visibly flattened at the poles. The figures for the equatorial and polar diameters are given in the Appendix. Saturn is also striped like Jupiter, but the stripes are less pronounced and clearly visible spots are not always present. On the whole Saturn shows a close resemblance to Jupiter, but its outer atmosphere is considerably quieter. This is due, no doubt, to its greater distance from the sun; Saturn receives only about $\frac{1}{90}$ of the light and heat received by the earth.

The few spots which do appear were the means of determining the period of rotation of Saturn. The spots were systematically observed for the first time by Sir William Herschel, who succeeded when Giovanni Domenico Cassini had failed.[1] In a paper of his which was read by somebody else to the Philosophical Society in January, 1794—Herschel never read his own papers to the society, possibly because he did not wish to waste his time with trips to London, possibly because he spoke English with a pro-

[1] Cassini tried in 1676, but had to say that the belts and possible spots in the belts were too faint to be seen clearly. Of course Herschel, a hundred years later, had a better instrument, but Cassini may simply have had the bad luck of trying to find spots at a time when there weren't any to be seen.

nounced German accent—he explained his method and gave his results. At first he had just noticed that the spots moved fairly rapidly. Then he noticed that the appearance of a given spot did not change much, so that he could recognize it as it came into view again. When he had located a portion of a belt with a reasonably pronounced spot near the center of the disk of Saturn he noted the precise time and then waited for it to appear again. It returned a little less than 810 hours later. Since it was already certain that the period of rotation had to be less than 11 hours, Herschel concluded that Saturn had rotated 79 times on its axis, which meant that one rotation took 10 hours, 15 minutes, and 40 seconds. Two other observations gave the figure of 10 hours, 16 minutes, and 51 seconds and a third set of observations resulted in 10 hours, 16 minutes, and 0.4 seconds.

For very nearly a hundred years Herschel's figures were accepted, rounded off to 10 hours, 16 minutes. There was little need to be more precise than that; besides, astronomers had other things to do, and good visible spots on Saturn are rare. But on December 7, 1876, a fine bright white spot appeared and Professor Asaph Hall in Washington, D.C., observed it for 61 rotations of the planet. This time the period of rotation came out as 10 hours, 14 minutes, and 23.8 seconds. Hall could cross check with five other American observers and was confident that his figure was correct.

By now we know that the period of rotation of a spot which is a disturbance in the atmosphere of the planet, does not necessarily have to be precisely the same as that of a point on the surface below. Jupiter's Red Spot has taught that lesson. In order to find the precise figure for the rotation of the surface one would have to soft-land a radio beacon somewhere along the planet's equator. Our spaceflight capabilities are still too new for such a mission although ten or fifteen years from now it might be done.

In 1876, when Asaph Hall observed his white spot, Saturn was thought to have almost as many moons as all the other planets put together. Mercury, Venus and Mars [2] were moonless, the earth had one, Jupiter four, Uranus four, and Neptune one, a total of ten moons. Saturn had eight, among them the largest satellite in the solar system, appropriately named Titan.

The story of these moons had been complicated, not because they are especially hard to see,

[2] The two tiny moons of Mars were discovered by Hall one year later, in 1877.

but because their discovery had been strung out over nearly two centuries.

The first one to be discovered was, as one would expect, the largest. It was found in 1655 by the Dutch astronomer and physicist Christiaan Huygens. He felt sure that there were no others, so he named it very simply *Luna Saturni,* the "moon of Saturn." The telescope used by Huygens (he had designed it himself), magnified 50 times, so that anybody who had a telescope of equal or greater power could see "Saturn's moon" easily.

Among those who looked for it was the astronomer of Louis XIV of France, Italian-born Giovanni Domenico Cassini. While looking for the moon discovered by Huygens he found another one that orbited the planet at a greater distance. Cassini was opposed to the suggestion by Marius and by Kepler that moons should be given names. He preferred to follow Galilei's example and therefore designated Huygens' moon S-I and his own S-II. The one he discovered was the one now named Japetus and the discovery had taken place in 1671.

So far, so good.

But the next year, in 1672, Cassini discovered still another satellite of Saturn, the one now called Rhea; the trouble was that this satellite moved inside the orbit of Huygens' moon. Cassini accepted the consequences of his decision to use numbers and renumbered all three of them. His latest discovery now became S-I, Huygens' moon became S-II and his own earlier discovery became S-III.

This was not yet the end, for in 1684 Cassini discovered two more moons of Saturn, the ones now named Tethys and Dione. Both of them orbited the planet at lesser distances than S-I. Cassini renumbered once more and Huygens' moon was now S-IV. Actually there were still more satellites of Saturn to be discovered, but not by Cassini. He died in 1712, at the age of 87, and had been totally blind for the last years of his life because doctors did not yet know what to do about cataracts.

The next two moons, now called Mimas and Enceladus, were found in 1789 by Sir William Herschel who was trying to disprove Cassini's ideas about the rings of Saturn. Herschel's two new moons moved still more closely to Saturn than the moons discovered by Cassini. Renumbering started all over again, but by then things were confused. If an astronomer said that he had observed S-III he had to specify which numbering system he employed, whether Cassini's second system or his third, or the renumbering that took place after Herschel's discoveries. The situation was even more complicated because there was at that time no journal devoted exclusively to astronomy, so that the various reports of discoveries appeared in a number of different "philosophical journals," published in different countries. The main article in such a journal might deal with a new attempt to decipher the hieroglyphs, followed by a report on some large bones discovered in a cave, and with a short notice that William Herschel had just announced the discovery of the sixth moon of Saturn tucked away somewhere in the back pages in fine print.

Fifty-nine years went by, then one more moon of Saturn was found by two astronomers. One was the American William C. Bond at Harvard Observatory, the other was William Lassell in England. Both were independent discoverers, but since Bond had seen it two nights earlier than Lassell it has become customary in the United States to call Bond the discoverer, while in Europe they say that this moon (Hyperion) was discovered by Bond and Lassell. This sounds as if the two had worked together—I have been asked once whether Bond was Lassell's assistant or the other way round. Now it so happens that this satellite has its orbit between two of the moons that were already known at the time—

which should have caused another partial re-numbering.

At that point Sir John Herschel (William Herschel's son) felt that this was too much adherence to a principle that did not work out well. Of course no one could say whether still another moon of Saturn might show up, but if it did the re-numbering would have to start all over again. Only names would help now; once the moons were firmly established by names an additional discovery would only add one more name instead of upsetting everything again. Sir John Herschel drew up a list from mythology of the names of the Titans, who were the relatives of Saturn. It was accepted by the various astronomical societies and is the one now in use.

Moon numero IX was added in 1898 by William H. Pickering. It was a discovery which caused quite a sensation. It boasted several "firsts." It was the first satellite to be discovered from South America (at Harvard's observatory near Arequipa in Peru) and it was also the first satellite to be discovered photographically instead of by direct observation. The plates proved that the new moon's orbit was about four times as great as that of Japetus, up to that moment believed to be Saturn's outermost moon. This great distance indicated an orbital period of over

500 days—more than six times the orbital period of Japetus. Pickering named "his" moon Phoebe, after one of the sisters of Saturn in mythology.

Phoebe was discovered "just in time" because Saturn then began to move into the constellations Scorpio and Sagittarius. These constellations contain a multitude of small stars, which would make the identification of one more small starlike object very difficult. After six years Saturn moved into a less crowded area and Pickering tried to find Phoebe again.[3] He did, in July, 1904, and in September of the same year the American astronomer E. E. Barnard saw Phoebe by using the largest telescope of the Yerkes Observatory. This produced a total of eight positions of Phoebe, strung out over six years, enough to compute the orbit. It was done by A. C. D. Crommelin of the Royal Observatory at Greenwich and what Crommelin then said caused some consternation.

That Phoebe was eight million miles from its planet was mainly a confirmation of earlier guesses. That Phoebe needed 550 days to com-

[3] In the course of this search he thought he had found a tenth satellite of Saturn which he named Themis, after another one of Saturn's sisters. But nobody else has ever found Themis so it seems that Pickering may have been mistaken.

plete one orbit was logical, considering the distance. That the orbit showed a high inclination (all the other satellites of Saturn move almost precisely in the plane of the rings) was a fact to be accepted. But Crommelin said that Phoebe was *retrograde!* If so, it was the first such body to be found in the solar system.

Our solar system is quite orderly in its motions. Seen from a point far above the earth's north pole everything moves counterclockwise. The sun rotates in that direction, all the planets move in that direction, all the moons move around the planets in that direction, and the planets spin on their axes in that direction. But Phoebe moved clockwise. The surprise was enormous, it had been taken for granted that there could be no exception.

Somebody who never revealed his identity even wrote a poem about this surprise:

> Phoebe, Phoebe, whirling high
>   In our neatly plotted sky,
> Phoebe, listen to my lay,
>   Won't you swirl the other way?
> Never mind what God has said,
>   We have made a law instead.
> Have you never heard of this
>   Nebular Hypothesis?
> It prescribes, in terms exact,

Just how every star should act.
Tells each little satellite
    Where to go and whirl at night
And so, my dear, you'd better change;
    Really we can't rearrange
All our charts from Mars to Hebe
Just to fit a chit like Phoebe.

Hebe, it must be added in explanation, is the name of one of the minor planets between the orbits of Mars and Jupiter, and no charts needed to be rearranged. One just had to realize that it is not a "law" that minor bodies in the solar system have to move counterclockwise. Such minor bodies can, on occasion, be pulled out of their orbits by a major planet and the result can be almost any kind of orbit.

Pickering's announcement of a tenth satellite of Saturn had been a mistake—but there is a tenth satellite of Saturn and its discovery in December, 1966, proved the practicality of using names rather than numbers. The newly discovered satellite is not farther away than the others; it is, in fact, the one closest to the planet, and it had escaped earlier discovery just because it is so close. The discoverer is the French astronomer Audouin Dollfus and he named it Janus, after a brother of Saturn.

The discovery was not accidental, as were the

discoveries of all the other moons of Saturn. It was the result of a short, but systematic search, undertaken for reasons that will be explained soon. Dollfus suspected that there might be a tenth moon. It had to be a small moon, or else it would have been discovered earlier. It probably had a normal orbit close to the rings. This meant that the best time to look for it was when the rings were not throwing too much light into the observer's eye or camera; in short, when they were edge on. It so happened that the rings of Saturn were edge on three times in 1966, on April 2, October 29, and December 17. Since the next edge-on view will not take place until 1981, Dollfus arranged to use the 43-inch telescope of the Pic du Midi Observatory in the Pyrenees.

"Three plates," Dollfus reported later in *Sky and Telescope* (September issue, 1967) "taken December 15, 1966 around 18:30 Universal Time [this is 1:30 P.M. Eastern Standard Time; naturally the United States were in daylight when the Pyrenees had night] revealed a very faint unidentified point of light lying exactly in the plane of the rings just beyond their eastern end. Had there been only a single photograph, the object could have been a [plate] defect or a star, but all three plates showed it, and it was moving closer to the planet. On the assumption that this was the expected satellite, I could make a first estimate of the radius of its orbit, and use this to calculate from Kepler's third law that the orbital period was 18 hours.''

If this object was a satellite of Saturn and if the calculated orbital period was about right, the object should have appeared on the western side of Saturn during the next night. Several plates were taken. The earliest of them did show the object where it was supposed to be. On the later plates it was obscured by the bright moon Titan which got in the way.

Flagstaff Observatory in Arizona confirmed the existence of Janus by plates taken on January 3, 1967; it was subsequently found on four more plates which had been taken by the French astronomer J. Texereau on October 19, 1966, at McDonald Observatory in Texas.

Is it possible that Saturn has additional undiscovered moons? It is, in the same sense that Jupiter may have undiscovered small moons far from the planet. Phoebe might have a friend or two in very large and inclined orbits. But there cannot be another undiscovered moon close to the planet, for a satellite inside the orbit of Janus would be in the rings.

Of the ten moons of Saturn four held surprises or taught important lessons. In order of discovery they are: Titan, Rhea, Phoebe, and Janus.

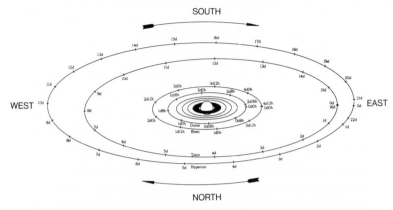

Fig. 10 The orbits of the inner satellites of Saturn, as they
will appear during the opposition in November,
1970. Iapetus and Phoebe are so far from the planet
that their orbits could not be shown. The diagram
was drawn before the existence of the tenth moon,
Janus, had been verified.

(From the *Nautical Almanac* for 1970)

Titan was long known to be the largest satellite
in the solar system, but something else was discovered quite late. In 1943, Gerard P. Kuiper
found that Titan has an observable atmosphere,
the only satellite in our system to have one. This,
of course, goes with the fact that it is the largest
satellite, it has the necessary gravitational force
to hold an atmosphere. The fact that it is so far
from the sun so that its atmosphere is hardly
heated helps a great deal. Small bodies, like satellites and even small planets, lose their atmospheres because of the energy received from the
sun. The molecules of an atmosphere move faster
when they are heated. If a satellite is small, the

molecules in its atmosphere may move fast enough to reach escape velocity when they are heated by the sun. Only a small number will reach escape velocity at any one time, but those that do depart from the satellite or small planet to take up an independent motion in space. In an atmosphere that is a mixture of gases, the light atoms are more likely to reach escape velocity than the heavy ones; for this reason atoms of the two lightest elements, hydrogen and helium, can escape and have in fact escaped from the earth's atmosphere, which keeps a tight grip on the heavier molecules like nitrogen, oxygen, and carbon dioxide.

One should expect, then, that the far below freezing atmosphere of Titan consists of relatively heavy molecules and this is the case. The main constituents are methane (marsh gas) and ammonia. The chemical formula for methane is CH_4, four atoms of hydrogen clinging to one atom of carbon. Since the weight of the carbon atom is 12 units and the hydrogen atoms weigh 1 unit each, the molecular weight of methane is 16. Ammonia is NH_3, one nitrogen atom of weight 14 and three hydrogen atoms, hence the molecular weight of ammonia is 17. Two still heavier gases are carbon dioxide (CO_2) and sulphur dioxide (SO_2); since the atomic weight of oxygen is 16 and that of sulphur is 32, the molecular weights of these gases are 44 for carbon dioxide and 64 for sulphur dioxide. Titan would be able to hold these two gases, but they have not been detected.

As for Rhea the surprise began with the discovery. Cassini found that it was fairly easily seen when to the west of Saturn but could never be seen when to the east of the planet. He drew the proper conclusion immediately: one hemisphere of Rhea must be much darker than the other hemisphere. Of course later astronomers have seen Rhea east of the planet, but it is true that Rhea has one light and one dark hemisphere; the dark portion reflects only about 20 percent as much light as is reflected by the light portion. The explanation probably is that about one half of Rhea's surface is covered with "snow" consisting of frozen gases.

Phoebe taught us the lesson that small bodies can be retrograde.

As for Janus the lesson is indirect.

Audouin Dollfus made the first estimate of its distance from the center of Saturn, namely 98,-000 miles, which may be 5000 or 6000 miles too high. It was immediately pointed out that this is dangerously close to "Roche's limit."

Most laymen are very proud of the fact that

they have heard of "Roche's limit" and even quote the figure: 2.44 radii of the planet in question. Inside that limit, they have read somewhere, "no moon is possible and Saturn's rings are proof of that." Multiplying the equatorial radius of Saturn by 2.44 gives 91,500 miles, while the outer edge of its rings is about 86,000 miles from the center of the planet. So you see clearly that the rings are inside the "limit" while Janus is just outside. But what is Roche's limit? And who was Roche?

Edouard Roche was a French-Swiss mathematician of the nineteenth century who, in 1850, published a paper on the relationship of a satellite and its planet. Roche investigated how the tidal forces produced by a planet would affect satellites at different distances. The term "tidal force" refers to the different degrees of gravitational attraction on various areas of the satellite's surface. Naturally the area of the satellite nearest the planet is attracted more powerfully than the area farthest from the planet. Roche found that at a distance of 2.44 radii of the planet, counting from the planet's center, the tidal forces would be powerful enough to tear the satellite apart.

This was a firmly ingrained belief and a few years ago I received an inquiry from a reader who had gone to work on the problem with pencil and paper. In the case of the earth, he had calculated, Roche's limit must be 9686 miles from the earth's center, or a little over 5700 miles from the surface. But virtually every artificial satellite orbits inside Roche's limit, some of them for as long as ten years and some quite flimsy, like the *Echo* balloon satellite which was made of very thin plastic.

Undoubtedly there was a discrepancy here. But what was wrong?

Had Roche made a mistake in his calculations?

I could assure him that Roche, as far as I could tell, had not made any glaring mistake. The mistake was hidden elsewhere and it consisted of the fact that the people who had written about "Roche's limit" ever since 1850, had not taken the trouble to look at Roche's original publication. They relied on what others had said about Roche and his "limit."

If they had looked at the original paper they would have seen that Monsieur Roche had been very careful in stipulating a "fluid satellite," meaning a satellite with no structural strength of its own.

Roche must have been aware that his calculations needed correction for the tensile strength of the material in a satellite composed of rock.

But not much was known about tensile strength in his time and the engineering calculations had not yet been invented. Hence he said a "fluid" satellite, but somebody who quoted from the original paper must have left out this important little word.

That there was a mistake somewhere might have been discovered in 1877 after Asaph Hall had determined that the inner satellite of Mars was quite close to the planet, only about 3700 miles from its surface or 5820 miles from its center. But that was still just outside Roche's limit, which lies at 5120 miles from the center of Mars. If that inner satellite, Phobos by name, had orbited 1000 miles closer to Mars, as it easily might, it would have been clear that the 2.44 radii limit did not apply to rocky bodies.

Well, the outcome of this discussion is that Saturn's rings are not, as has been asserted so often, the outcome of Roche's limit, unless the satellite that was supposed to have been torn apart to make the rings consisted of a large heap of fluffy snow.

But let us take the case systematically which is to say chronologically. Galileo Galilei thought he had seen two large moons. Other early observers got a somewhat better but still unclear picture. Saturn seemed to have handles like a teacup, and since the Latin word for handle is *ansa* they began to speak of the *ansae* of Saturn. Modern astronomers know better, of course, but they find the term useful for descriptive purposes and still speak of the *ansae*. It was Huygens who saw the rings clearly but since they were unique he hesitated to say so. He composed a Latin sentence

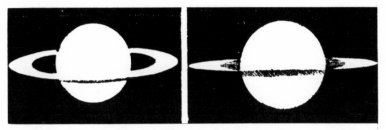

Fig. 11   Two drawings of Saturn made by Christiaan Huygens in 1656 and 1657—the first correct interpretation of the rings.

which described what he saw. It read: *Annulo cingitur, tenui plano, nusquam cohaerente, ad eclipticam inclinato*. In English: It is encircled by a ring, thin and flat, nowhere touching, inclined to the ecliptic. But he did not publish the sentence, he dissected it into its letters and published it as aaaaaaa ccccc d eeee and so forth. Nobody could read it unless Huygens explained what it meant and if he had found himself mistaken he probably would not have explained it. If he was correct, however, that jumble of letters would prove that he was the first to make the discovery.

The next discovery was that there was not merely one ring around the planet, but two! Cassini, in 1676, was the first to make a drawing showing that a dark line ran around the middle of the ring. He concluded that the black he could clearly see was the black of space, seen through a division between the two rings. It is called Cassini's Division to this day.

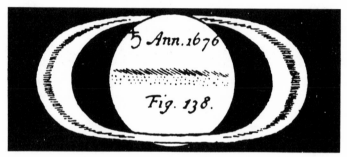

Fig. 12   Drawing of Saturn made by G. D. Cassini, showing the dark line which is now known as "Cassini's Division."

The next step, also taken by Cassini, was to make a guess as to the nature of the ring, or rings. The rings were large but very thin and Cassini could not imagine that anything of that shape could be a solid body. In 1705 he stated that it was most likely that the whole ring consisted of swarms of tiny moonlets, too small to be seen individually. This is what it actually is, except that the "moonlets" are far smaller than Cassini imagined.

Though he was right, he did not convince everybody.

William Herschel, who preferred visual evidence to theories, began by saying that there was only evidence for a ring (singular) with a "black belt." Whether that black belt was a division between two rings was only a possibility, but there was no evidence. So far Herschel had only seen the ring from the north, he would wait until he had seen its southern exposure before coming to a decision. Eleven years would go by until Herschel would be able to see the other side of the ring; in the meantime he worked on the black belt, making certain that its width always remained the same and that it always stayed in the same position. By 1791, after long observations of the other plane of the ring, he dropped the designation "black belt" and decided that Saturn "had two concentric rings." But he also said that it would be nice if one could see a star through Cassini's Division; only then could one be really sure.

Later a star was seen through Cassini's Division, but that was on February 9, 1917, long after Herschel's time.

While Herschel had slowly come around to accept a double ring he still thought that it was solid and others agreed. Occasionally an observer would even discover a "mountain" on Saturn's rings; actually just especially bright spots. There are also thin spots in the rings. One of them goes by the name of Encke's Division. If one goes through a pile of observers' reports they will see that many observers say that they looked hard for Encke's Division but could not find it, while others claim that they saw it clearly. The ones who saw it are in the minority, but that does not prove that they are wrong. Encke's Division apparently only sometimes exists.

It became customary to call the outer ring Ring A and the inner ring Ring B. Ring A had two sharp edges, one on the outside and one along Cassini's Division. Ring B had a sharp outer edge, along the Division, but its inner edge was not so sharp. In 1850, when Saturn was in a favorable position for such observation it turned out that there was something very tenuous which circled the body of the planet within the inner edge of Ring B. Again, the discovery was made by Bond and the confirmation came from Lassell. The tenuous innermost ring should have been called Ring C, but Lassell, in a letter to the Astronomer Royal, referred to it as the crepe ring, looking for a descriptive term. Most astronomers used it, crepe ring was a far better expression than "Ring C."

Soon after the discovery of the crepe ring the nature of the rings was definitely settled by the Scottish mathematician James Clerk Maxwell. He showed that the rings had to rotate, otherwise they would break up and fall to the surface of the planet. They could not be solid, because if there were only two rings they would be disrupted by tidal forces. If there were more than twenty concentric solid rings, as had been suggested, they might stay in one piece, but then they would not look the way they looked. The idea that the rings might consist of liquid was also disproved. Maxwell ended up with the explanation that had been advanced by Cassini, that the rings had to consist of a very large number of small bodies, each orbiting the planet with a velocity that would keep it in orbit at the distance it happened to have.

Now that the nature of the rings had been settled the next step was to explain the existence of Cassini's Division. The explanation was supplied by the American astronomer Daniel Kirkwood in 1867, ten years after Maxwell had shown that the rings had to consist of freely orbiting matter.

Kirkwood calculated the orbital period of a

particle moving in the center of Cassini's Division. It would need 11 hours and 20 minutes to complete one orbit. But such a period is about one half of the orbital period of Mimas, one

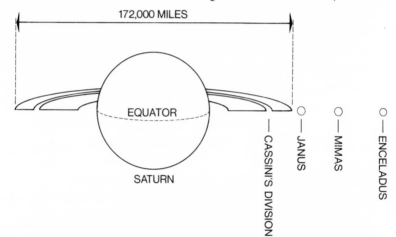

Fig. 13   The dimensions of the ring system and the distances of the three innermost satellites of Saturn. The distance from the inner edge of the crepe ring to Saturn's cloud layer is about 12,500 miles; the overall width of the ring system happens to be very nearly equal to one radius of Saturn.

third of the orbital period of Enceladus, a quarter of the orbital period of Tethys and one sixth of the orbital period of Dione. This means that such a particle would be regularly disturbed by not less than four different satellites, each of them tending to push it out of that particular orbit. In time the four satellites succeeded in pushing everything out of that region. The particles that had been forced out either found a place in one of the other two rings, or, if they collided with another particle, lost so much velocity that they entered the atmosphere of Saturn and became a part of the planet.

Now there remained only two things to be settled. One was the thickness of the rings, the other was the average size of the particles that composed the rings. A third problem was comparatively minor: some observers thought they had noticed that the center of the rings did not coincide precisely with the center of the planet, in other words that the rings were a little eccentric. The years 1894 and 1895 were good for settling this question and E. E. Barnard did settle it. The rings are not eccentric, but sometimes they are seen in such a position that they look as if they were.

As for the size of the particles and the thickness of the ring the two problems were obviously interconnected. If the thickness of the ring were found to be, say, 30 miles (Barnard had said "less than 50 miles") then each particle had to be smaller than that.

The observation of 1917 provided a clue.

Saturn, moving across the area of the constellation Gemini, covered up ("occulted" is the technical term) a star of the seventh magnitude with its rings, though not with its body. A star of the seventh magnitude is one that people with excellent eyesight can just see during a clear and moonless night; in a telescope it is a very bright star. The orbital motion of Saturn made it look as if the star entered Ring A at a slant, then shone through Cassini's Division and then re-entered Ring A once more, finally to come out again and shine outside next to Ring A. Two observers in different observatories in England watched the performance; one of them saw all of it, while the other picked up the star as it was shining through Cassini's Division.

The important point was, however, that it could be seen not only when shining through the Division, it could be seen all the time. The ring was too thin to blot it out completely. One of the observers described its occasional dimming in the following manner: if you call its brightness outside the ring 100 percent it was quite close to that brightness when shining through the Division. When shining through the ring its brightness was 25 percent, but twice it moved up to about 50 percent.

This observation proved, first, that there were thin spots, as the sporadic reports about Encke's Division had already indicated. But it could also be used to make a good estimate of the particle size. Crommelin proceeded as follows: if a particle in the ring had had a diameter of around 2000 feet it would have looked as large as the observed star when seen from earth. The star, shining through a ring consisting of 2000-foot "particles," would have looked as if it were flickering. There would also have been flickering, somewhat less pronounced, if the particles had had a diameter of 1000 feet. But the star had only been dimmed, it had not flickered. Hence the particles composing the ring had to be much smaller than 1000 feet in diameter.

This, of course, brought the thickness of the ring down to less than 1000 feet and more reduction was to come.

Drs. Allan Cook and Fred Franklin of the Smithsonian Astrophysical Laboratory at Cambridge, Massachusetts, studied about a thousand pictures of Saturn taken from an observatory in South Africa, using photoelectric devices to measure the brightness of the planet's body and of the rings. While the plates were being taken, the relative positions of the rings, of the earth, and of the sun changed, resulting with changes in brightness. This set of changes could be used to calculate the relationship of the diameter of the rings to their thickness.

The outside diameter of Ring A is 172,000 miles and the inside diameter of Ring B is 110,000 miles, so that the width of the rings, including Cassini's Division, is about 62,000 miles. Now the ratio of the width of the ring to the thickness was found to be 356.4 million to 1. The result is less than one foot for the thickness of the rings. Since most astronomers think that the rings consist, in the main, of ice crystals, such a low value for the thickness is possible.

Of course it is surprising.

But it makes the sight of Saturn's rings even more marvelous than before.

Oh yes, how about Janus?

Why did Dr. Dollfus suspect that there had to be one more moon?

Well, if the explanation for Cassini's Division worked out by Kirkwood was correct, the "resonance" of half the period of Mimas should be in the center of the Division. Many books say that it is, but in reality it is near the inner edge of the Division. To make the Division be what it is an unknown satellite was needed, one close to the outer edge of Ring A.

One could not make an ironclad promise that Janus would be found.

But it was.

CHAPTER FOUR

"THE FIRST COMET OF 1781"

The date was March 13, 1781, a Tuesday.

The place was Bath in England.

The time was 10 P.M. local time and the weather was unpleasant. It was chilly and gusty and the air felt moist. But the sky was clear and William Herschel, then 43 years old, was out in the open by his telescope, observing. The telescope was trained on a star in the constellation Gemini, labeled *H Geminorum,* which is not a very luminous star.

Herschel was using *H Geminorum* only for reference that night, he was more interested in the still weaker stars in its vicinity. Suddenly he saw a star that should not have been there, one that no astronomer had ever listed on his charts. And it was not a faint little star, it was larger in appearance than *H Geminorum*. "I suspected it to be a comet," he wrote about a month later when he sent a report to the Royal Society in London.

Being probably the most experienced astronomical observer of his time, Herschel knew a simple trick. In his telescope the main mirror—which he had cast, ground and polished himself—could not be changed, but the eyepiece was built in such a way that different sets of lenses could be quickly inserted and removed. When finding the new object Herschel had used an eyepiece with a magnification of 227. He had other eyepieces with magnifications of 460, 932, 1536 and 2010 close at hand. He pulled out the eyepiece with a magnification of 227 and inserted the one with a magnification of 460.

Increasing the magnification under these circumstances should have produced several results. The stars that had been visible with the lesser magnification would seem to be farther apart from each other, but they would remain pinpoints of light. A few weaker stars that had not been visible before would probably appear in the now smaller field of vision; but that was unimportant. But the suspected comet, if it was one, would appear larger than a point of light. It did, it now showed a definite disk. Herschel went on to the next more powerful eyepiece; again the fixed stars moved farther apart but remained pinpoints of light, while the disk of the comet looked still larger. Being a systematic man, Herschel moved on to the highest magnifications he had. The comet began to look hazy under these high magnifications and did not have a good outline. Herschel knew that this was the fault of his telescope: the main mirror did not gather enough light to permit the use of the highest magnifications on this particular object.

He felt certain now that he had discovered a comet. There followed a few nights when the sky was not clear, but on March 19, Herschel was able to observe his comet again. By the end of the month it seemed to be a bit larger, which would be the case if the comet was on its way to its perihelion, the point closest to the sun along its orbit. On April 6, he observed it once more and noted that it was perfectly round, had a sharp edge and no sign of a tail.

Then he wrote a report to the Royal Society.

The French astronomer Alexandre-Gui Pingré was then at work on a book he called *Cometographie* (it appeared three years later), which is one of the biggest books on comets ever written. In it he listed William Herschel's discovery as "the first comet of 1781" but began the section about it with the words: "this comet or planet." Other astronomers who had been informed had looked for the comet and had had no difficulty finding it. But by then several months had gone by since Herschel's original observation and the comet could be expected to have grown a tail by then. It hadn't. But it had moved some distance in that time and since its positions during successive observations were precisely known one might compute an orbit for it. Of course that orbit would have to be corrected later, but it would be nice to have a preliminary calculation as a starting point.

Anders John Lexell did the mathematical work and found that the observations so far indicated a nearly circular orbit, something that would be most unusual for a comet. And the observations fitted into the calculation if you assumed that this circular orbit was at a distance of 19 A.U. from the sun. Lexell could not imagine a comet moving in a circular orbit at 19 A.U. and in July, 1781, he stated that William Herschel had been wrong to assume that he had discovered a comet. He had done something far more important: he had discovered a planet! The first planet to be discovered since antiquity.

When Johann Elert Bode in Germany heard about the circular orbit at 19 A.U. he was most pleased for a personal reason. Some years earlier another German, Johann Daniel Titius, had found an interesting mathematical fact. If you began with 0.4 and added 0.3 multiplied by zero you still had 0.4 as the result. Then 0.4 was added to 0.3 multiplied by 1, with 0.7 as the result. Then you took 0.4 and added 0.3 multiplied by 2 and you got the result 1.0. But this sequence of 0.4, 0.7 and 1.0 expressed the distances of the planets Mercury, Venus and earth from the sun. Carrying this farther you got the distance of Mars, Jupiter, and Saturn, always expressed in A.U.[1]

Titius never explained how the idea occurred to him, nor do we know just why this is so.

The Titius rule had a value of 2.8 in it, which would lie between the orbits of Mars and Jupiter. No planet to fit into this gap was known then, but Bode concluded (correctly) that an explanation of its absence would be found in time. What made him happy was that, according to the Titius rule, the figure that followed after Saturn was 19. It was the distance of the new planet. Bode, in his elation, publicized the Titius rule so much and so often that it is now known as the Bode-Titius rule. Bode also suggested the name

[1] For Titius' formula and a table see the Appendix.

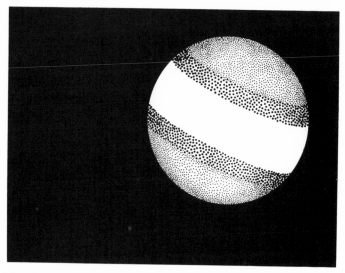

Fig. 14   The planet Uranus as it appeared in 1915 through a powerful telescope.

Uranus for the new planet. And he thought of something else.

The new planet was large and luminous enough to be visible to the naked eye as a very faint star when it was in opposition. Uranus will be in opposition January 13, 1970, in the constellation Virgo. But anything that the naked eye can just see is conspicuous in a telescope, even a small one. It was quite possible that earlier astronomers had seen Uranus and thought that it was a fixed star. The planet would have an orbital period of close to 84 years and if it stayed close to the ecliptic, as the existing observations indicated, it would be easy to calculate where it must have been in the sky during a given year.

Bode made himself a list of such approximate positions for a century before the actual discovery of the planet and began to check through older astronomical books to see whether somebody had drawn a star chart of a section of the sky where Uranus had been. Almost immediately he discovered that Uranus had been entered as a "star of the sixth magnitude" in 1690 by John Flamsteed, the first Astronomer Royal of England. The German astronomer Johann Tobias Mayer had also listed it as a star in 1760.

After Bode's discovery of earlier records of Uranus, other astronomers went to work on the same quest. A German scientist found that Bode had not checked Flamsteed's works carefully enough. Flamsteed had, in fact, seen Uranus a total of five times. And a French astronomer, Alexis Bouvard, checking the work of his compatriots, found a total of ten observations by Pierre Charles Lemonnier. In addition to three observations which Lemonnier had discovered when he reviewed his own charts. If Lemonnier had been half as careful and systematic as Herschel, he surely would have received credit for the discovery of Uranus instead of Herschel.

Bouvard also undertook a comprehensive calculation of the orbit of Uranus. For this purpose he classed all the observations since Herschel's discovery as "modern observations," while he called the prediscovery observations "ancient observations," even though the oldest of them was only about a century old. With observations, even unwitting ones, extending over a full century, the job should have been easy. The more observations, the better. But then Bouvard ran into an entirely unexpected difficulty. The ancient observations (1690–1770), and the modern observations (1781–1820), did not agree. Uranus could not possibly have been seen in the places where some observers had entered it on their charts.

It was logical to assume that the recent observations were more precise. The instruments were better and the observers knew what they saw; they did not casually notice a "star" that other astronomers had failed to list. But when Bouvard based an orbit calculation on the recent observations only, he found that the older positions were rather far off. It was not quite believable that the earlier observers could have been so careless. Bouvard said that future mathematicians would have to find a method for reconciling the two sets of observations. Or, he added, it might be found that "a foreign and unperceived cause" had been acting on the planet. The words "unperceived cause" were just a careful way of phrasing it. What he meant was that the differences might be due to the gravitational attraction of an undiscovered planet.

What an undiscovered planet would do to the orbital motion of Uranus is fairly easy to imagine. The unknown planet would, of course, move at a greater distance from the sun in a larger orbit. Naturally its orbital velocity would be slower than that of Uranus. When both planets were in the same sector of their orbits, Uranus would gradually "catch up" with the unknown planet. They would mutually attract each other. Because of the attraction of the unknown planet Uranus would move a little faster in its orbit than it would if the unknown planet did not exist. It would be speeded up a bit—the other one, at the same time, would be slowed down but since it is still unknown that would not be observed. Because Uranus moves faster, it would eventually overtake the unknown planet, at which time the action of their gravitational fields would be reversed: Uranus would move a little more slowly than it should, while the unknown planet would move a little faster.

We do not know whether Bouvard had this explanation in mind. Perhaps he imagined, instead, a change in the sun's gravitational field at such long distances. It is something he did not say. Others, however, about 20 years later, took the hint, and their work eventually led to the discovery of Neptune.

In the meantime Uranus presented a few more puzzles.

The period of its rotation on its axis was not yet known, but because both Jupiter and Saturn rotated rapidly one could assume that Uranus did the same. In that case it should not look precisely round but show a flattening at the poles. Herschel stated that he had seen a polar flattening, but later observers failed to see it. To them Uranus looked perfectly round as, say the full moon. Since Herschel was known to be a most careful observer they could only shake their heads and hope that an explanation would be found.

Just in the case of Uranus Herschel *had* made a mistake, but it had nothing to do with the polar flattening. Uranus has moons, as expected, and in 1787 Herschel reported two of them, now known to be the two outermost of the five moons of Uranus.[2] Somewhat later Herschel reported

---

[2] Two others were discovered by William Lassell in 1851, while the fifth, which is the one nearest to the planet, was found by Gerard P. Kuiper in 1948.

that he had found four more moons, bringing the total to six. Here he was deceived by small fixed stars that showed near the planet; Uranus happened to be in an area of the sky where such stars are numerous.

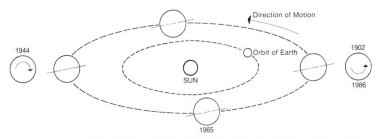

Fig. 15   The orbit of Uranus and how it will appear when seen from earth. In 1902 and in 1944 we have a "pole on view" of the planet, making it appear circular. This will repeat in 1986. In 1923 and 1965 the flattening was at its most pronounced. (Flattening is exaggerated in the diagram.)
March, 1970.

When Herschel announced his discovery of the moons of Uranus, ten other moons were known: our own, the four large moons of Jupiter and five of the moons of Saturn. (Two years later Herschel discovered two more of Saturn's moons.) Each and every one of these moons had its orbit over the equatorial regions of its planet. The moons of Uranus seemed to be an exception. Observers tried to doubt their eyes and did their calculations over several times. But finally even the most skeptical of them had to admit: the moons of Uranus seemed to be in polar orbits. They did not orbit over the planet's equator, but orbited over a meridian, going nearly over its poles. This, however, was a serious mistake.

The first man to suspect the truth was the famous French mathematician Pierre Simon, Marquis de Laplace, who lived from 1749 to 1827. Late in life—we do not know precisely when—he wrote that he felt certain that the moons of Uranus move over the planet's equator. Since the planes of the orbits of these moons were found to be nearly vertical to the ecliptic it followed that the axis of Uranus was tilted to the same extent.

It needed courage to say so, since the axes of the other planets do not show much tilt. Jupiter's axis of rotation is tilted by only 3 degrees of arc measured from a line perpendicular to the plane of Jupiter's orbit. The axis of our own planet is tilted by 23½ degrees of arc, the axis of Mars is tilted a little more (25 degrees of arc), and that of Saturn still a little more, namely close to 27 degrees of arc. If Laplace was right—that is, if the orbits of the moons actually indicated the degree of the axial tilt—the axis of Uranus would deviate from the plane of its orbit by only 8 degrees of arc, an unheard-of tilt of 82 degrees. Actually the tilt is 98 degrees of arc, 8 degrees more than a right angle.

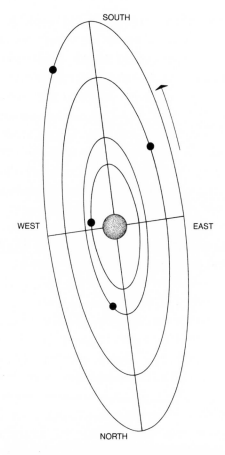

Fig. 16 Diagram of the orbits of the four major moons of
Uranus for March, 1970.

(From the *Nautical Almanac* for 1970)

Somebody should have realized that Laplace's
idea also explained why Herschel, in one of his

late papers on Uranus, had said that the planet was flattened and why later observers had not been able to confirm that point. As Uranus travels around the sun, its axial tilt does not change. And its axis will always point in the same direction. This has the result that an observer on earth will sometimes see the planet with one of its poles in the approximate center of the disk. When seen in that position, Uranus will look perfectly round, since the planet's equator is at the rim of the visible disk. At other times we have a side view of Uranus, with the equator going roughly across the center of the disk. In that position the polar flattening will be visible.

Nobody seems to have drawn this conclusion, or if somebody did, he did not say so.

In 1839 an astronomer would have had a perfect side view of Uranus. The actual observation had been made two years earlier, by Johann Heinrich von Mädler who had been active in Berlin as an observer of the moon. Around the year 1837 Wilhelm Struve, director of the Observatory of the University of Dorpat,[3] had called von Mädler to Russia. It was there that

[3] Dorpat is now called Tartu and is in Esthonia; at the time of Struve the University of Dorpat, supported financially by the Czar, called itself "a German university on Russian soil" and the Czar did not object.

the polar flattening of Uranus was actually measured for the first time.

Von Mädler found that the polar diameter of the planet was about 10 percent shorter than the equatorial diameter, but the main point was that somebody now had actually seen that the planet's axis was very nearly in the same position as its orbit. All in all he made 330 diameter measurements in 18 nights of observation. In his report he urged astronomers to try to find spots on the surface of the planet; this had not been done up to that time and he himself had not succeeded in observing any. In other words, the period of rotation of the planet was still unknown. The telescopes were not yet good enough, and Dorpat /Tartu is in an area where the weather, while occasionally beautiful and clear, is frequently bad.

It was not until 1870, almost precisely a hundred years after the discovery, that markings on the disk were first seen, appropriately enough by English observers. But the markings were too uncertain to be drawn. A thorough survey of "the Uranian System" concerned mainly with the orbits of the satellites and the flattening of the planet was conducted by Professor Simon Newcomb in Washington, D.C., in 1873.

About twenty years later the Italian astronomer Giovanni Virginio Schiaparelli tried his luck with Uranus. He also said he could see markings, but refused to publish his drawings— complaining that it was all too indistinct, he complained. Really good drawings were not made until early in the current century. They show that Uranus has a pronounced wide, light belt around its equator, flanked by two darker stripes, corresponding to what, on earth, are the temperate zones. Beyond the darker stripes the polar areas are lighter again, but not as light as the equatorial region. The color of Uranus is a faint blue, though sometimes it is faintly greenish-blue.

The temperature of the upper layers of the atmosphere of Uranus must be very low, since the planet receives only $\frac{1}{370}$ the amount of sunlight per square mile that strikes the earth. What the light belt around its equator is, is unknown. Why the axis has its strange position is unknown too.

But the problem of the irregularities of its orbital motion were largely solved around the middle of the last century.

CHAPTER FIVE

NEPTUNE AND ITS FORMER MOON

Alexis Bouvard had hinted that the irregular motion of Uranus might indicate the existence of another planet in 1821. We now know that one year later, in 1822, Uranus actually overtook Neptune; during that year the sun, Uranus, and the still-unknown Neptune formed a straight line in space, with Uranus between the two other bodies.

Since the two planets remained relatively close to each other for several years their mutual attraction was quite pronounced. On earth, astronomers only saw with dismay that the "errors" mounted up, as Uranus deviated more and more from its calculated position. In 1834 the vicar of Hayes in Kent, the Reverend T. J. Hussey, suggested that these "errors" might provide the basis of a calculation of the position of the unknown planet. And in 1840 the famous astronomer Friedrich Wilhelm Bessel in Königsberg in East Prussia told a lecture audience that his pupil Friedrich Wilhelm Flemming was working on this problem and would soon be finished. As it turned out Flemming never finished his work, he suddenly fell sick and died soon after the date of Bessel's lecture at the early age of twenty-eight.

At that time Sir George Biddell Airy was Astronomer Royal of England and consequently he was at the center of astronomical activities. He received a letter from Eugène Bouvard, the nephew of Alexis, which contained the words: "does this suggest an unknown perturbation . . . by a body situated farther away? It is my uncle's idea." Airy himself was not certain; he was inclined to think that the law of gravitation might not be complete. It worked well for the inner planets of the solar system and even for Jupiter and Saturn. But perhaps if the distances were much greater one would have to apply a correction. It seems from Airy's statements and his behavior during the years to come that he would have preferred to discover a minor flaw in the law of gravitation and to find the correction needed. It so happened that in this he was completely wrong.

In 1841 a twenty-two-year-old student of astronomy at Cambridge, England, read a report on the "errors" in the orbital motion of Uranus and decided that the cause must be an unknown planet. He also decided that he would calculate its position. The name of the student was John Couch Adams.

He had one "fact" to go by. According to the Bode-Titius rule the unknown planet had to be at a distance of 39 A.U. Everything else he had to guess. Was the orbit of the unknown planet inclined to the ecliptic to the same degree as that of Uranus? One could not know, but in order to begin somewhere, this was the assumption Adams made. (Actually it is almost precisely one degree of arc greater.) And what was the size, or rather the mass, of the unknown? Again Adams assumed that it might be the same as that of Uranus; that assumption happened to be very nearly true, by coincidence, of course.

He made a preliminary calculation whose only purpose was to show whether an unknown planet *could* explain the difficulties with Uranus' orbit. The answer was "yes." He talked to Professor

John Challis about his idea and asked whether the professor could obtain the precise figures for the discrepancies from the Royal Observatory at Greenwich. Professor Challis wrote to the Astronomer Royal and as soon as the mails of that time could carry it, a voluminous bundle arrived in Cambridge. Adams now had the raw material and he made his calculations for a date in the future, namely for October 1, 1845. He finished barely in time, about three weeks before that date. Challis was impressed but he did not do the natural thing and check on the predicted area with a telescope. Instead he gave Adams a letter of recommendation to the Astronomer Royal. Adams went to Greenwich himself and tried to see the Astronomer Royal personally but that proved to be impossible. The Astronomer Royal was a busy man. Adams left his manuscript with a house servant, went back to Cambridge and hoped that Sir George Biddell Airy would find the time and have the inclination to read it.

Airy did read the manuscript and wrote to Adams as well as to Professor Challis. In the letter to Adams he quibbled, asking whether Adams could explain by his theory why the distance of Uranus from the sun also was not quite what the calculations said it should be. In the letter to Challis he said that Adams could be wrong, but he added that that would not be the fault of Adams, since all these discrepancies could be due to a failure of the law of gravity.

During the same year (1845) competition arose in Paris. The director of the Paris Observatory was Dominique François Jean Arago, a careful astronomer, a good physicist, and a versatile man. For a short time Arago had been Minister of War of France; he had seen to it that slavery in the French colonies was abolished, and he was fairly active in French politics all his adult life. In his capacity as director of the Observatory he was unhappy with Uranus and, one day, he summoned a younger astronomer whom he knew to be an excellent mathematician into his office. When the younger man, Urbain Jean-Joseph Leverrier, appeared, Arago asked him what he was doing at the moment. Leverrier replied that he was investigating comet orbits.

Arago said that the comet orbits could wait, the orbit of Uranus was more important. Needless to say Leverrier went to work, beginning with a tabulation of calculated and of actual positions of the difficult planet. If Leverrier suspected the influence of an unknown planet he did not say a word about it in his first paper on Uranus. He only presented facts.

In his second paper, published in June, 1846,

he said in so many words that only an undiscovered planet could explain the behavior of Uranus. He also gave its probable position. On reading this paper, Airy became nervous. Leverrier had never head of Adams, but Airy had and if he remembered the figures Adams had given him, he must have realized that both Adams and Leverrier were in close agreement. The positions for the unknown planet given by the two mathematicians differed by only one degree of arc!

In July, 1846, Airy wrote to Challis, asking him to begin observing in accordance with the calculations of Adams. If the explanation of the strange behavior of Uranus was an unknown planet instead of a flaw in the law of gravitation, Airy wanted that planet to be a British discovery. Challis felt that he had to obey Airy, but he was convinced that it would take a long time, so he delayed beginning.

Meanwhile Leverrier had refined his own work some more and felt quite sure of himself. There was only one small problem and he went to Arago to discuss it. The best telescope on the European mainland was that of the Royal Prussian Observatory in Berlin and Johann Gottfried Galle was known to be a fine observer. Should he ask the Prussians to search for the planet?

Arago felt that it would still be a French discovery and agreed. On September 18, 1846, Leverrier wrote to Galle. Galle had to go to his director, Johannes Franz Encke to ask for permission. Encke probably reasoned that it would be a Prussian discovery if Galle found the planet and agreed immediately.

The weather in Berlin can be quite rainy in September, but the evening was fine and Galle did not want to waste it. He called his assistant, Hermann Ludwig d'Arrest, and they agreed to meet after dark. The plan was simple. Galle would point the telescope at the place in the sky indicated by Leverrier and would do the actual observing. The assistant sat with a printed star chart of the area in such a position that the light of his desk lamp could not be seen by Galle. Galle would call out to him which stars were in his field of vision and d'Arrest would check them off on the chart. They probably started with the brightest stars in the telescope's field.

Not quite one hour after they had started Galle called out a star of the eighth magnitude in such and such a position, and d'Arrest called back: *nicht auf der Karte* (not on the chart). Neptune had been discovered and Galle, even during the first night, had no doubt that the star that was not on the chart actually was a planet.

The date was September 23, 1846; the delay of five days since Leverrier had posted his letter was due to the fact that a letter took five days to travel from Paris to Berlin.

There was jubilation in Berlin and in Paris, and dismay in Greenwich and in Cambridge, where the bad news arrived on October 1. Of course Challis was scolded for his lack of diligence. When it was discovered that Challis, during the time he had searched, had seen and entered Neptune four times without realizing that it was a planet, he was scolded even more.

England, after the first shock had worn off, did her best to give Adams belated honors. The Queen offered to knight him, but he preferred to remain Mr. Adams. The Prime Minister offered to make him Astronomer Royal after Airy had died or resigned, whichever came first. Adams would have had a long wait. Sir George Biddell Airy did not resign until 1881 and did not die until 1892. By a coincidence, Adams died the same year. But he did accept a professorship at Cambridge and did succeed Challis as the director of the observatory.

There was, as could be expected under the circumstances, some international quibbling about who should be considered the "discoverer" of Neptune. Since Galle had only followed instructions and since Adams' work had not led to success, Leverrier got the honor. Being the official discoverer he had to name the planet. He suggested the name Neptune. Even that led to more quibbling. Arago insisted that the planet should be named Leverrier and Leverrier himself was not unwilling. But astronomical tradition won out; planets receive mythological names and Neptune it was, is, and will be.

Since Neptune is not hard to see in a good telescope everybody remembered what had happened with Uranus. Had there been "pre-discovery observations" of Neptune? There had been one, just one, by Joseph-Jérôme de Lalande on May 10, 1795.

The question of whether Neptune had moons was not debated, so to speak, for lack of time, because William Lassell discovered a moon of Neptune on October 10, 1846, only 17 days after the discovery of the planet itself.

It was given the name Triton, a fitting name for a companion of Neptune.

Triton is a large satellite, its diameter is in excess of 3000 miles. Its orbit is nearly circular and lies 220,000 miles from the center of the planet. The orbital period is 5 earth days and 21 hours. The odd fact is that this normal, if big, satellite in its normally shaped orbit does do what the satellites of Uranus were mistakenly thought to do: it follows a polar orbit.

More than a hundred years after the discovery of Triton it turned out that Neptune has a second satellite, discovered by Gerard P. Kuiper in 1949 and named Nereid. (The Nereids were classical sea nymphs.) Nereid is a small satellite with a diameter of approximately 200 miles and a strange orbit. When closest to Neptune, Nereid is 800,000 miles from the planet's center; at its farthest point it is 6 million miles distant. It takes 359.88 days to complete this long orbit.

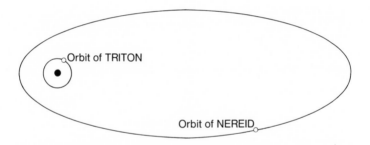

Fig. 17   The nearly polar orbit of Triton and the six-million mile orbit of Nereid. Below is a perspective drawing of the orbits.

110

Speaking of odd orbits, the orbit of Neptune, regular though it is, also displays an oddity; it is at the wrong distance. When beginning their calculations both Adams and Leverrier relied on the Bode-Titius rule and assumed a distance of 39 A.U. In the course of their work both men found that a planet at that distance would be too slow-moving to produce the effects on which their calculations were based. Hence both assumed that

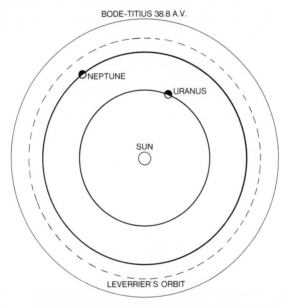

Fig. 18   The suspected orbit of Neptune at 38.8 A. U.; the orbit of Neptune at 34 A. U. as predicted by Leverreier and Adams, and the actual orbit at 30 A. U.

the unknown planet might be 5 A.U. closer than the Bode-Titius rule had predicted. After Neptune had been actually seen and observed for some time so that its orbit could be calculated exactly, the distance turned out to be still less, only 30 A.U.

We clearly have a collection of unusual facts at the edge of the solar system. Uranus is "lying on its side," yet the orbits of its moons are properly over its equator, as if the whole "Uranian System," as Simon Newcomb called it, had been tilted through 98 degrees of arc after it was formed. We have Neptune as the only violator of the Bode-Titius rule. We have one of Neptune's moons in a polar orbit and another one that has the most elongated orbit of anything in the solar system, except for a number of comets.

Is there anything else odd out there?

There is, and its name is Pluto.

Originally it was called the trans-Neptunian planet, or just trans-Neptune. One Mr. David P. Todd carried out a telescopic search for it during 1884, probably by examining carefully each of the constellations of the zodiac. The search was fruitless.

Todd was not the only one who hoped to become famous by discovering a planet, but he was the first to devote telescope time to it. Others, led by Leverrier himself, speculated. There were many "ifs" in the speculation but the speculation itself was justified.

Both Adams and Leverrier had done their work by starting out with the differences between the observed positions of Uranus and the positions which it should have occupied if it had been the outermost planet of the solar system. Then each invented a planet, a planet which had the right size and mass, and the right orbit, to explain the discrepancies. Whether Neptune had the right size and mass remained to be established; it was already clear that it did not have the right orbit. However, since Neptune was closer to Uranus than the two mathematicians had assumed, it was conceivable that it could produce the observed effects on the motion of Uranus with a smaller mass.

A period of waiting was called for. Maybe Neptune could account for everything, even if it differed from the "calculated planet" of Adams and Leverrier. Maybe it could not, in which case the calculated planet was actually two planets.

Most astronomers seem to have hoped that the calculated planet would turn out to be two planets, so that another discovery would be waiting somewhere in the depths of space. Those that hoped for two planets could point to one fact that had been established by the ever-active Professor Simon Newcomb of the U.S. Naval Observatory. One can calculate the mass of a planet from the motion of its moons.

To explain this let us turn the example around.

Back in 1928 a retired Austrian army engineer by the name of Potočnic was thinking about what later came to be called a "synchronous satellite." A synchronous satellite, such as the ones now used for long-range communications, moves in an orbit above the equator, at just the right rate to keep pace with the rotation of the earth. Seen from the turning earth it looks as if it were hanging motionless above one point of the equator.

Captain Potočnic wanted to know how far such a satellite would have to be from the earth's surface and how fast it would have to move. He found that the surface-to-satellite distance would have to be 22,300 miles and that the orbital velocity of the satellite would be 1.9 miles per second. To make this calculation he needed to know the mass of the earth, which had been determined by various methods. If the earth were more massive than it actually is, the synchronous orbit would be nearer and the orbital velocity would have to be higher. These calculations suggest the way in which the mass of a planet and the orbital distance of a satellite with a certain orbital period are related.

In fact, if the orbital distance and orbital period of a moon are known from observation, it is possible to calculate the mass of the moon's planet. Professor Newcomb calculated the mass of Neptune from the orbit of Triton. Then he calculated the mass of Neptune, using its actual distance from the sun, and from the influence it exerted on the motion of Uranus. Obviously the two figures should have been the same, but they were not. Calculating from the orbit of Triton, he found that it would take 19,380 Neptunes to equal the mass of the sun. Calculating from the influence on Uranus, it would take 19,700 Neptunes to equal the sun's mass.

So there was a discrepancy, and the simplest explanation was another undiscovered planet. And since the position of one unknown planet had been successfully calculated there seemed to be no reason why this performance could not be repeated.

Of course the work would be far more difficult, in part because no irregularities in the motion of Neptune had yet been observed. In 1884, when Todd made his search, Neptune had been observed for less than a quarter of its orbit; if there were irregularities they had not yet shown.

After all, the unknown planet might, during that time, have been clear across the solar system in the opposite sector of its orbit where it would have no influence on Neptune.

Hence the theorists had to go back to Uranus, which had been observed for more than one of its orbits since its discovery by Herschel. The calculation had to go through a number of stages. First the orbit of Uranus would be calculated as if the sun and Uranus were the only bodies in space. Then the orbit would have to be corrected for the influence exerted by Saturn, the next planet on the inside. Then it would have to be corrected for Jupiter's influence. (The smaller planets near the sun, Mercury, Venus, earth, and Mars could be disregarded, because they were both small and far away.) Then came the correction for Neptune's influence. After all that was done there either would be, or would not be, small discrepancies between the calculated and the observed motion of Uranus. And from these "residuals" one might find the position of a still unknown planet.[1] The weakest point was the "correction for Neptune" because not very much of its actual orbit was then known.

Even the most impatient theorists simply had

[1] This is an explanation of the principles involved. The actual calculation would be somewhat different.

to wait if they wanted their work to be meaningful. But by 1905 Neptune had been observed for about one half of its orbit. And at that time a new astronomical tool was available, the photographic plate.

The two men who devoted the largest amount of time and effort to the search for the trans-Neptune were both Americans. One was a professional astronomer, William H. Pickering. The other was Percival Lowell of Boston who had retired from business—more or less—to devote his time, his money, and his considerable energy to astronomy. He had built his own observatory in Arizona where the skies are clear most of the time.

From there he hunted the unknown planet for two years by a photographic survey. His method was this: he would photograph a certain region of the sky, exposing the plate for three hours to make faint objects register. During these three hours the telescope was moved slowly by a clockwork drive, to compensate for the rotation of the earth. Three days later he would photograph the same region of the sky, again with an exposure time of three hours. Then the two plates would be compared with a magnifying glass. If the unknown planet had been caught, it should have moved a little during the three-day interval.

Of course each pair of plates showed that something had moved. There are usually several small comets in the sky which would show motion. Then there are many tiny planets (called variously minor planets, planetoids, or asteroids), which move between the orbits of Mars and Jupiter and always get in the way of such a survey. But they are easy to eliminate because their orbital velocities are between 8 and 11 miles per second, much too fast for the unknown trans-Neptune. Then there are among the fixed stars various kinds of variable stars that are sometimes brighter than at other times and which, therefore, might show on one plate but not on the other. Lowell's survey was completed in 1907, after two years of work. The result was zero, nothing unknown had been found.

Lowell decided that it might be better to launch a mathematical attack first. It would be tedious work but hardly more tedious than the two years spent on the photographic survey. And it was likely to tell him where to look.

Pickering started his mathematical work at about the same time, and it was published by Harvard University in 1909. Lowell's mathematical work was finished in 1914 and published by him in 1915. Before publication he had a second photographic search started, probably hoping to add an account of the actual discovery to the publication.

The rivalry between Pickering and Lowell began to look like the race between Adams and Leverrier, with Lowell having the advantage of his own observatory.

But history did not repeat itself.

Lowell died on November 12, 1916, ending his second search.

A third search was undertaken by Mount Wilson Observatory near Los Angeles in 1919, using Pickering's calculations. It was as fruitless as Lowell's searches.

On March 13, 1930, the anniversary of the discovery of Uranus and also Percival Lowell's birthday, the Lowell Observatory sent out the news that the trans-Neptunian planet had finally been discovered.

The actual discovery had been made on February 18 by Clyde W. Tombaugh, who was comparing plates taken on January 23 and January 29 of that year. The plates showed a region of the constellation Gemini where Herschel had found Uranus, except that the star on which the plates were centered was *delta Geminorum,* the fourth brightest star in that constellation. After Tombaugh had found a suspicious object that had moved exactly the right distance during the six days between photographs, more pictures of the area were taken. Again the suspected planet was found, and it had again moved the right distance during the time between photographs.

Other observatories verified the discovery and Lowell Observatory decided on a name. They chose Pluto which was appropriate mythologically and also provided an opportunity for honoring Percival Lowell's memory by making the symbol of the new planet **P**, combining the letters P and L.

Pluto, when seen through a sufficiently powerful telescope, looked yellowish. It also looked very small. It certainly did not look like the expected trans-Neptune, large and greenish and somehow impressive. The orbital motion did indicate that it was farther from the sun than Neptune; it also indicated immediately that it did not conform to the Bode-Titius rule.

Half a year of observation was enough to show something else that was decidedly peculiar. Pluto, at the time of its discovery, was near the ecliptic, as the trans-Neptune was expected to be. But it did not stay in the ecliptic; it moved through it at a pronounced slant. When Percival Lowell made his first search he would probably have found it if it had been in the same position as in 1930. But in 1905 it had been so far below the ecliptic that Lowell's plates probably did not cover the area where it was hiding. The inclination of Pluto's orbit was at least 14 degrees of arc, which was very strange for a planet. Later the figure for the inclination had to be upgraded to 17 degrees of arc.

Pluto was much smaller than expected, cer-

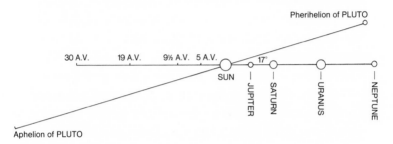

Fig. 19   The orbit of Neptune seen edge-on, with the distances for the four gas giants. The inclined line is the orbit of Pluto seen edge-on, showing both its inclination and extent. Below the orbits are shown in perspective.

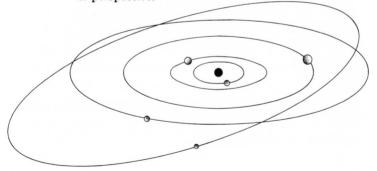

tainly not more than 6000 miles in diameter, which is smaller than the earth's diameter. Continued observation also showed that the orbit was not only strongly inclined, but elongated as well. All of this just did not go with the preconceived ideas of the trans-Neptunian planet, and Pluto threatened to become an astronomical repeat of the geographical story of Timbuktoo.

Timbuktoo was once a fabulous city in Africa. No explorer had seen it himself, but African traders, most of them Arabs, told of "golden Timbuktoo." The city was rich and prosperous and probably large. Retelling increased its population and its riches. Beautiful gardens were added and the buildings in these gardens were believed to be white castles in a splendid Moorish style. Several explorers set out for golden Timbuktoo. Some had to turn back, some perished on the way. Finally Timbuktoo was reached. It consisted of less than a hundred miserable huts. There were no gardens, there was nothing that could even be called a "building." The population was small and poor. And the climate was awful.

Compared to what Lowell had hoped to find, Pluto not only threatened to be an astronomical Timbuktoo; it was one.

Twenty years after the discovery, Gerard P.

Kuiper succeeded in measuring its diameter and found it to be even smaller than had been feared, namely 3600 miles.

The whole structure of Lowell's calculation collapsed because of this measurement. Lowell had started out with the belief that a planet about seven times as massive as the earth was needed to explain what had been observed. It was shown later that so much mass was not needed: a planet not much more massive than the earth might have had the same effect. But if a planet with a diameter of 3600 miles were to have as much mass as the earth, each cubic inch of it would have had to weigh as much as 60 cubic inches of water. There is no substance in existence that dense. The heaviest metal, osmium, is only 22½ times as heavy as water. On the other hand, if you assume that Pluto has the same density as the earth (5.5 times that of water, which makes the earth the densest planet in the solar system); its mass would be only ten percent that of the earth, far too little to exert any influence on planets as big as Uranus and Neptune.

Let us summarize at this point what was known about Pluto when Kuiper measured its diameter. Its inclination to the ecliptic is 17 degrees of arc. The aphelion of Pluto is 4567 million miles from the sun or 49.3 A.U., its perihelion 2766 million miles or 29.8 A.U. When at perihelion Pluto is closer to the sun than Neptune; it is the "outermost planet" only for a part of its orbit. At the moment Pluto is on its way to its perihelion, which it will reach in 1989. Since its orbital period is 248.43 years it will reach aphelion again in 2113.

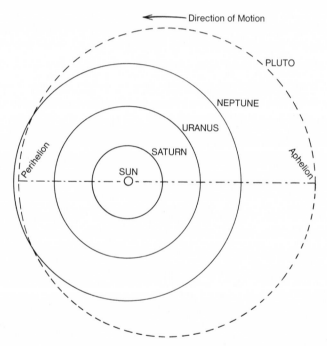

Fig. 20   The orbits of the outer planets and the orbit of Pluto (broken line) projected on the plane of Neptune's orbit.

Does Pluto rotate on its axis?

Since its disk, even in a big telescope, is so small, direct observation could not answer this question. But it could be done in another way, by measuring the brightness of Pluto with sensitive photo-electric devices over a period of time. If Pluto has surface markings that are too small or too faint to be detected by the eye, they would still cause minor variations in overall brightness. These variations would also be undetectable by looking at it, but they would register on such a photo-electric instrument.

In 1955 Kuiper had three different sets of such measurements, one of which he had taken himself. Comparing them carefully he found that the variations in brightness indicated a period of rotation of 6.39 days.

This was unusually long for a planet far from the sun. But it would be a quite reasonable period of rotation for a satellite; remember that for all moons the period of rotation and the orbital period are the same. The conclusion was inevitable: Pluto was a "runaway moon" of Neptune, which continued to rotate at the rate of 6.39 days after it had been flung into an orbit around the sun. The rate of rotation indicates that it was somewhat farther from Neptune than Triton when it was still a moon.

Now here was one more proof of the occurrence of a past "event" at the edge of our solar system. That "event" tilted Uranus and its system of moons, it tilted the orbit of Triton, it caused Nereid to go into its present, "unreasonable" orbit. And it "detached" Pluto from Neptune.

All of which leaves us with a complete mystery. Everybody agrees on the "event," but nobody has been able to think of what it could have been. One is tempted to think of another sun passing fairly close, but that should also have affected Saturn, which has the most perfect system of satellites. If we learn more about the edge of the solar system beyond Neptune we might find facts which could lead to an explanation of the "events." Until then all speculation is useless.

CHAPTER SIX

BEYOND THE ORBIT OF NEPTUNE

During the summer of 1960, I delivered a series of lectures to a group of New York City school teachers who had to bring their scientific knowledge up to date. The Space Age was just beginning. A number of artificial satellites had been put into orbits around the earth; the Russians had succeeded in sending one space probe past the moon and had hit the moon with another one. The result of all this was that the teachers had to take a course so that they would be able to answer the questions of their pupils.

In one of these lectures I mentioned that Pluto had been found to be a former moon of Neptune and that the true planet beyond Neptune was still to be discovered. During the discussion after the lecture one of the teachers wanted to know why astronomers were so sure that there actually is a planet beyond Neptune.

The answer is that nobody can be sure that there is such a planet. We simply do not know the number of condensation centers in the cosmic cloud from which our solar system was formed.

But let us approach the problem systematically, beginning with the question of a trans-Neptune's probable distance from the sun. Here the Bode-Titius rule is the only guide we have. The two figures beyond the distance of 38.8 A.U. where Neptune was supposed to be are 77.2 A.U. and 154 A.U. Was the sun's gravitational pull sufficient to keep a planet in the solar system at such distances?

The answer to that question is yes. The sun could still hold a planet in orbit at a distance of about 30,000 A.U., so it is obvious that it could do so at 154 A.U.

But could we see a planet orbiting at such a distance?

Well, we know how much light such planets would receive from the sun. The planet at a distance of 77.2 A.U. would receive only $\frac{1}{5960}$ the amount of light that is received by the earth, square mile for square mile. The planet at a distance of 154 A.U. would receive only $\frac{1}{23,716}$ of what the earth receives. But distance is not the whole story. The size of the planet and its albedo are also important and here we have to guess. If Neptune were moved to a distance of 77.2 A.U. it would appear about as luminous as Pluto does now. This means that it would show up on a photographic plate but does not necessarily mean that it would be recognized. Pluto was first recognized because of its motion, but Neptune in the the more distant orbit would move much more slowly.

If Neptune were moved to the distance of 154 A.U. it is almost certain that it could not be recognized as a planet. It would move more slowly still. And while it might still register on a photographic plate, that plate would also show thousands and thousands of equally faint objects.

Of course one may question whether a trans-Neptune planet has to be at either 77.2 A.U. or 154 A.U. from the sun. After all, Neptune turned out to be nearly 9 A.U. closer to the sun than "permitted" by the Bode-Titius rule. Couldn't the next planet beyond Neptune orbit the sun at a distance of 45 A.U. or 50 A.U.? Since we do not know why Neptune is closer than expected there is no way of denying the possibility.

In 1902 the German astronomer Theodor Gri-gull suggested that there might be a planet at a distance of 50 A.U. which would have an orbital period of 360 years. Only a few years later the American astronomer Thomas Jefferson Jackson See thought that three planets beyond Neptune might be found: one at 41.25 A.U. with an orbital period of 272 years; one at 56.0 A.U. with an or-bital period of 420 years and one at 72.0 A.U. with an orbital period of 610 years. William H. Pickering suggested one at a distance of 51.9 A.U. with an orbital period of 373.5 years.

Let us mention here the orbital periods for planets located at the two distances beyond Nep-tune predicted by the Bode-Titius rule. The planet at 77.2 A.U. would need slightly more than 680 years to complete one orbit while the planet at 154 A.U. would require 1911 years for one orbit.[1]

The long orbital period of the more distant of these two hypothetical planets is the reason why it was said above that its image on a photo-graphic plate, even if it should register, would al-most certainly not be recognized for what it is. A

[1] Calculating these figures is relatively easy: you cube the figure for the distance and then find its square root. In the case of the planet at 154 A.U. the cube is 3,652,264 and the square root of this figure is almost precisely 1911. This short cut is based on Kepler's Third Law.

planet always announces its nature by motion against the field of far distant fixed stars. Our known outer planets already present difficulties in that respect; let us see what these motions are or would be:

DISTANCE IN A. U.	ORBITAL PERIOD (years)	YEARLY MOTION (degrees of arc)
19 (Uranus)	84	4.3
30 (Neptune)	164	2.5
77.2	680	0.53
154	1911	0.18

The width of the full moon in the sky is just about half a degree of arc, so the planet at 77.2 A.U. would need an entire year to move the width of the moon across the sky and the planet at 154 A.U. would need about three years. In addition to low luminosity and ultra-slow motion there is still the problem of where to look. All the planets out to Neptune have orbits that are approximately in the plane of the ecliptic, so that they are seen against the background of one of the constellations of the zodiac. In the case of Pluto this is no longer true.

Since the unknown event at the edge of the solar system tilted the orbit of Pluto by 17 degrees of arc we have to consider the possibility that the orbit of a planet beyond Neptune might be tilted to the same extent or even more so. In that case any discovery that might be made would be the result of pure chance and not the result of a systematic search. Remember that even Pluto has to be considered a chance discovery, although it took place because of a systematic search.

In spite of all these pessimistic statements there is a reason for us to believe in the existence of a planet beyond Neptune. Planets betray their existence not only by being visible but by something they do. If circumstances are favorable, they change the orbits of comets.

Comets are believed to orbit the sun in very large numbers a very long distance away, maybe at 30,000 A.U. Every once in a while one, or several of these comets, leaves the so-called comet cloud and approaches the sun along a very narrow elliptical orbit. In the normal course of events it then makes a loop around the sun and disappears in space, its orbit leading it back to the comet cloud from which it came. But if such a comet on its way (either toward the sun or away from it), passes fairly close to a large planet, its orbit will be changed. As a rule it is severely shortened. The new orbit betrays which planet caused the orbital change because the aphelion of the new orbit is near the orbit of the planet that disturbed the original orbit. Usually the aphelion of the new comet orbit is somewhat farther from the sun than the orbit of the planet.

If, for example, you find a comet with an orbit that has its aphelion at 6 A.U. or 7 A.U. you can be certain that Jupiter (orbiting at 5.2 A.U.) caused the change. All the comets that have had their orbits changed by Jupiter are collectively known as Jupiter's "comet family."

Going by this example the existence of a "comet family" whose aphelia are grouped at a certain distance should be a pretty good indication of the existence of a planet. In 1900 five comets with aphelia far beyond the orbit of Neptune were known, which is the reason why Theodor Grigull suspected the existence of a planet at 50 A.U.

In 1948 Dr. Karl H. Schütte undertook the job of going through all the astronomical journals, looking for comets with reasonable known orbits that had distant aphelia. He found thirteen and to his surprise they fell into two groups, one group with aphelia at distances ranging from 47.6 A.U. to 59.0 A.U.; the other with aphelia from 75 A.U. to 89 A.U. (A condensed form of his table can be found in the Appendix.)

However, the case is not quite as strong as the

aphelion distance alone would indicate. If these comets really formed two "families"—that is, if they were caused by two different planets—their orbits should have about the same inclinations. But in the group with aphelia around 50 A.U. two have very high inclinations, two have inclinations that are low (for comets, that is) while one is an in-between case. In the second group, the one with aphelia beyond 77 A.U., the picture is somewhat clearer. With the possible exception of Comet Dodwell-Forbes these inclinations *could* be due to one and the same planet.

The mean of all the inclinations of the second group is 47.3 degrees of arc. Leaving out Comet Dodwell-Forbes the mean is raised to 50.6 degrees of arc. This might indicate that the planet itself has an orbit with an inclination of at least 40 degrees of arc.

Putting everything together we can say this: it seems likely that there is a planet at the Bode-Titius distance of 77 A.U. Its luminosity cannot be high, but the inclination of its orbit probably is. It might be discovered, but this will require a lucky accident.

THE GAS GIANTS, Main Characteristics

Name	Mean Distance (A.U.)	From Sun (mill. mi.)	Diameter (miles)	Period of Rotation (hrs./min.)	Sidereal Orbital Period (years)	Orbital Velocity (mi. p. sec.)	Inclination to Ecliptic	Density (water = 1)	Mass (earth = 1)
Jupiter	5.20	483.4	88,700 (82,790)	9 hrs. 55 min.	11.86	8.1	1.3°	1.33	318.0
Saturn	9.539	886	75,100 (67,170)	10 hrs. 14 min.	29.46	6.0	2.5°	0.69	95.2
Uranus	19.18	1782.0	29,200	10 hrs. 49 min.	84.01	4.2	0.8°	1.56	14.6
Neptune	30.06	2792.0	27,700	14 hrs. 0 min.	164.08	3.4	1.8°	2.27	17.3

The figures in parentheses under the heading Diameter for Jupiter and Saturn are the polar diameters. All other figures are equatorial diameters.

Figures supplied by Hayden Planetarium

THE BODE-TITIUS RULE

It is not known when Johann Daniel Titius found his rule, which he published in 1770 in the German edition of a French philosophical work. It remained little-known until publicized a few years later. Titius had given it in the shape of the formula $0.4 + (0.3 \times 2^n)$ where n took the values— 0, 1, 2, 3, 4, etc. Written as a table it looks like this:

			Planet	Mean Distance	
$0.4 + (0.3 \times 2^0)$	=	0.4	Mercury	0.39	A.U.
$0.4 + (0.3 \times 2^1)$	=	0.7	Venus	0.72	A.U.
$0.4 + (0.3 \times 2^2)$	=	1.0	Earth	1.00	A.U.
$0.4 + (0.3 \times 2^3)$	=	1.6	Mars	1.52	A.U.
$0.4 + (0.3 \times 2^4)$	=	2.8	Ceres *	2.77	A.U.
$0.4 + (0.3 \times 2^5)$	=	5.2	Jupiter	5.2	A.U.
$0.4 + (0.3 \times 2^6)$	=	10.0	Saturn	9.54	A.U.
$0.4 + (0.3 \times 2^7)$	=	19.6	Uranus	19.18	A.U.
$0.4 + (0.3 \times 2^8)$	=	38.8	Neptune	30.06	A.U.
$0.4 + (0.3 \times 2^9)$	=	77.2	—	?	
$0.4 + (0.3 \times 2^{10})$	=	154.0	—	?	

Ceres is a minor planet

Figures supplied by Hayden Planetarium

THE MOONS OF JUPITER

No.	Name	Mean Distance From Planet's Center (miles)	Orbital Period (days)	Diameter (miles)	Year of Discovery and Name of Discoverer
V	Amalthea	112,000	11 hrs. 57 min.	100 *	1892; E. E. Barnard
I	Io	262,000	1 day 18 hrs. 28 min.	2,020	1610; G. Galilei
II	Europa	417,000	3 days 13 hrs. 14 min.	1,790	1610; G. Galilei
III	Ganymede	665,000	7 days 3 hrs. 43 min.	3,120	1610; G. Galilei
IV	Callisto	1,171,000	16 days 16 hrs. 32 min.	2,770	1610; G. Galilei
VI		7,133,000	250 days 14 hrs. 00 min.	50 *	1904; C. D. Perrine
VII		7,295,000	259 days 16 hrs. 00 min.	20 *	1905; C. D. Perrine
X		7,369,000	263 days 13 hrs. 00 min.	10 *	1938; S. B. Nicholson
XII		13,200,000	631 days 2 hrs. 00 min.	10 *	1951; S. B. Nicholson
XI		14,000,000	692 days 12 hrs. 00 min.	10 *	1938; S. B. Nicholson
VIII		14,600,000 R	738 days 22 hrs. 00 min.	10 *	1908; P. J. Melotte
IX		14,700,000 R	758 days 00 hrs. 00 min.	10 *	1914; S. B. Nicholson

R means "retrograde"

* estimated, not actually measured

Figures supplied by Hayden Planetarium

THE MOONS OF SATURN

No.	Name	Mean Distance From Planet's Center (miles)	Orbital Period (days/hours)	Diameter (miles)	Year of Discovery and Name of Discoverer
X	Janus	100,000	0 days 17 hrs. 59 min.	300	1966; A. Dollfuss
I	Mimas	116,000	0 days 22 hrs. 37 min.	300	1789; Wm. Herschel
II	Enceladus	148,000	1 day 08 hrs. 53 min.	400	1789; Wm. Herschel
III	Tethys	183,000	1 day 21 hrs. 18 min.	600	1684; G. D. Cassini
IV	Dione	236,000	2 days 17 hrs. 41 min.	600	1684; G. D. Cassini
V	Rhea	327,000	4 days 12 hrs. 25 min.	810	1672; G. D. Cassini
VI	Titan	759,000	15 days 22 hrs. 41 min.	2,980	1655; C. Huygens
VII	Hyperion	920,000	21 days 06 hrs. 38 min.	100	1848; Wm. C. Bond
VIII	Iapetus	2,213,000	79 days 07 hrs. 56 min.	500	1671; G. D. Cassini
IX	Phoebe	8,053,000	550 days 11 hrs.	100	1898; Wm. H. Pickering

R means "retrograde."

NOTE: Unlike the moons of Jupiter which are numbered in the sequence of their discovery, the moons of Saturn were renumbered in the order of their distance from the planet; this system has been ruined by the discovery of the tenth moon which is closest to the planet.

Figures supplied by Hayden Planetarium

THE MOONS OF URANUS

Name	Mean Distance from Planet's Center (miles)	Orbital Period (days)	Diameter (miles)	Year of Discovery and Name of Discoverer
Miranda	77,000	1 day 9 hrs. 56 min.	200	1948; G. P. Kuiper
Ariel	119,000	2 days 12 hrs. 29 min.	500	1851; Wm. Lassell
Umbriel	166,000	4 days 3 hrs. 38 min.	300	1851; Wm. Lassell
Titania	272,000	8 days 16 hrs. 56 min.	600	1787; Wm. Herschel
Oberon	365,000	13 days 11 hrs. 07 min.	500	1787; Wm. Herschel

The names for the satellites were proposed by Sir John Herschel. *Oberon* and *Titania* were, of course, taken from Shakespeare's *A Midsummer-Night's Dream*, but *Ariel* was not taken from *The Tempest*. *Ariel* and *Umbriel* were taken from Pope's *The Rape of the Lock* where Umbriel is called "a dusky sprite." The name was picked because Umbriel is so hard to see. The still-fainter *Miranda* was named by its discoverer, and this time the name is from *The Tempest*.

Figures supplied by Hayden Planetarium

TWO GROUPS OF COMETS THAT MAY BE "FAMILIES."

Designation and Name			Perihelion (A.U.)	Aphelion (A.U.)	Orbital Period (years)	Inclination to Ecliptic (degrees)
1862	III	Tuttle-Swift	0.962637	47.6	119.64	113.56
1889	III	Barnard	1.102397	49.8	128.31	31.22
1917	I	Mellish	0.190186	55.0	145.34	32.68
1939	VI	Rigollet	0.7485	57.2	156.04	64.20
1907	II	Grigg-Mellish	0.923279	59.0	164.32	109.84
1857	IV	C. W. F. Peters	0.746842	75.3	234.6	32.77
1932	X	Dodwell-Forbes	1.1308	80.8	262.1	24.50
1931	III	Nagata	1.0469	82.0	267.5	42.30
1885	III	Brooks	0.7491	83.7	274.5	59.10
1905	III	Giacobini	1.114640	88.0	297.2	40.21
1932	I	Houghton-Ensor	1.2544	88.7	302.0	74.28
1932	V	Peltier-Whipple	1.037210	89.1	302.5	71.71
1874	IV	Coggia	0.675783	89.1	302.0	34.14

Figures supplied by Hayden Planetarium

Achilles, 48–49
Adams, John Couch, 103–104, 106–109, 111, 113, 119
Airy, Sir George Biddell, 102, 104, 106, 108
Albedo, 21–22, 129
Angular Momentum, 14
Ansae, 75
Aphelion, 123, 132–133
Arago, Domique Francois Jean, 105–107, 109
Asteroids, 10, 118
Astronomical Unit, 7
A.U., 7–9

Barnard, Edward Emerson, 46, 64, 81
Belts, 26
Bessel, Friedrich Wilhelm, 102
Bode, Johann Elert, 89, 91
Bode-Titius Rule, 89, 103, 111–112, 120, 128–130, 134
Bond, William C., 62, 78
Bouvard, Alexis, 91–93, 101
Bouvard, Eugene, 102
Burke, Dr. B. F., 42

Callisto, 45
Carbon dioxide, 70–71
Cassini, Giovanni Domenico, 27, 34, 43–47, 60–62, 76–77, 79
Cassini's Division, 76–80, 82, 84
Cerenkov, Pavel Alexeyevitch, 43
Cerenkov Radiation, 43
Ceres, 10
Challis, Professor John, 103–104, 106, 108
Coblentz, F. W. W., 38
Comet, 86–88, 132–134
Comet Dodwell-Forbes, 134

Cometographie, 87
Cook, Dr. Allan, 83
Crepe Ring, 78–79
Creti, Donati, 36
Crommelin, A. C. D., 64–65, 83

Dark Companion, 5–6
d'Arrest, Hermann Ludwig, 107
Dawes, Rev. William R., 35
de Lalande, Joseph Jerome, 109
Dione, 61, 80
Distribution of Angular Momentum, 14
Dollfus, Audouin, 66–67, 71
Dorpat, University of, 98–99

Earth, 6–7
Ecliptic, 22, 120
Enceladus, 61, 80
Encke, Johannes Franz, 107
Encke's Division, 78, 82
Europa, 45
Explorer XXXVIII, 42

Flagstaff Observatory, 68
Franklin, Fred, 42, 83

Galileo Galilei, 43–44, 54–55, 60, 74
Galle, Johann Gottfried, 106–108
Ganymede, 45
Gas Cloud Theory, 13
Gas Giants, 10
General Natural History and Theory of the Heavens, 11
Gravity, 11
Grigull, Theodor, 130, 133

H Geminorum, 85–86
Hall, Professor Asaph, 58–59, 74

Halley, Dr. Edmund, 8
Harvard Observatory, 62
Hebe, 66
Herschel, William, 28, 57–58, 61–63, 77–78, 86–88, 91, 94–95, 97, 116, 119
Hooke, Robert, 34
Hussey, Rev. J. T., 102
Huygens, Christiaan, 43, 60, 70
Hyperion, 62

Inclination (of planets' orbits), 22
Inertia, 11
Inner planets, 6
In conjunction, 23
In opposition, 23
Io, 45

Janus, 66–69, 71–72
Japetus, 60, 63–64
Jeffreys, Dr. Harold, 38–39
Jupiter, 7, 19–53, 55–57, 59, 96, 116, 133

Kant, Immanuel, 11
Kant-Laplace Theory, 13, 15
Kepler, Johannes, 8, 45, 60
Kepler's Third Law, 68, 130
Kirkwood, Daniel, 79, 84
Krakatoa, 37
Kuiper, Gerard P., 69, 110, 123, 125

Lagrange, Joseph Louis, 50
Lampland, C. O., 38
Laplace, Pierre Simon, Marquis de, 12, 96–97
Lassell, William, 62, 78, 109
Lemonnier, Pierre Charles, 91
Leverrier, Urbain Jean-Joseph, 105–109, 111–113, 119
Lexell, Anders John, 88
Lick Observatory, 47
Lowell Observatory, 119–120

Lowell, Percival, 117–120, 122–123

Marius, Simon, 44–46, 60
Mars, 7, 20, 55, 59, 74, 96
Maxwell, James Clerk, 79
Mayer, Johann Tobias, 91
McDonald Observatory, 68
Mean interval of oppositions, 24
Melotte, P. J., 47
Menzel, Donald H., 38
Mercury, 6, 20, 55, 59
Methane, 70
Mimas, 61, 80, 84
Minor planets, 10
Mt. Wilson Observatory, 47, 119

Neptune, 10, 20–21, 25–26, 59, 94, 101, 107–109, 111–118, 123–133
Nereid, 110, 126
Newcomb, Professor Simon, 99, 112, 114–115
Newton, Sir Isaac, 11
Nicholson, Seth B., 47

Orbital period, 7–8
Orbits (see Planetary orbits)
Outer planets, 6

Paris Observatory, 105
Patroclus, 51
Perihelion, 124
Perrine, Charles Dillon, 47–48
Phobos, 74
Phoebe, 64, 68–69, 71
Pickering, William H., 63–64, 66, 117–119, 130
Pic du Midi Observatory, 67
Plane of the ecliptic (see Ecliptic)
Planetary orbits, 22

Planetoids, 118 (*see* also Asteroids)
Pluto, 112, 120–127, 129, 131–132
Potocnic, Captain, 114
Principia Mathematica, 11

Radiation formula, 8
Radio noise, 42–43
Raft theory, 37
Ramsey, Dr. W. H., 39–40
Red spot, 33–37, 59
Reese, E. J., 29–31
Retrograde, 65
Rhea, 60, 69, 71
Ring A, 78, 82, 84
Ring B, 78, 84
Ring C, 78–79
Roche, Edouard, 72–73
Roche's Limit, 71–74
Römer, Ole, 44
Rotational period, 30
Royal Observatory at Greenwich, 47, 64, 104
Royal Prussian Observatory, 106
Royal Society, 86–87

Sagan, Professor Carl, 52
Saturn, 9, 20–25, 54–59, 61, 63–64, 66–68, 71–72, 74–75, 77–78, 81, 84, 96, 116, 126
Schiaparelli, Giovanni Virginio, 100
Schutte, Dr. Karl H., 133
Schwabe, S. H., 35
Secondary atmosphere, 17
Shain, Dr. C. A., 42
Simon, Pierre, Marquis de Laplace (*see* Laplace)

Sky and Telescope, 67
Smithsonian Astrophysical Laboratory, 83
Struve, William, 98
Sulphur dioxide, 70–71
Sun, 55
Synchronous satellite, 114
Synodic period, 24
System I, 29
System II, 28–29, 31, 42

Tethys, 61, 80
Texereau, J., 68
Tidal force, 72
Titan, 59, 66, 69–71
Titius, Johann Daniel, 89
Todd, David P., 112, 115
Tombaugh, Clyde W., 119
Transit, 8
Trans-Neptune (*see* Pluto); 112, 119–120
Triton, 109–110, 115, 126
Trojan asteroids, 51

University of Heidelberg Observatory, 48
Uranus, 9, 20–21, 25–26, 59, 90–96, 98–101, 103–106, 110, 112–113

Velocity of light, 43
Venus, 7, 19–20, 55, 59
von Madler, Johann Heinrich, 98–99

Wildt, Dr. Rupert, 39
Wolf, Professor Max, 48, 51

Yerkes Observatory, 64

Zodiac, 22
Zones, 26

ABOUT THE AUTHOR

WILLY LEY died on June 24, 1969, as this book was going to press. He was a well-known author and scientist. His numerous books cover various scientific subjects. An engineer, he was a member of the German Rocket Society, the A.A.A.S., and other major scientific societies. He has written for McGraw-Hill Junior Books INSIDE THE ORBIT OF THE EARTH and VISITORS FROM AFAR: THE COMETS.